Assessment Program C

VISIONS

Language ✧ Literature ✧ Content

Mary Lou McCloskey

Lydia Stack

Australia ✧ Canada ✧ Mexico ✧ Singapore ✧ United Kingdom ✧ United States

VISIONS ASSESSMENT PROGRAM C
Mary Lou McCloskey and Lydia Stack

Publisher: *Phyllis Dobbins*
Director of Development: *Anita Raducanu*
Developmental Editor: *Tania Maundrell-Brown*
Associate Developmental Editor: *Yeny Kim*
Associate Developmental Editor: *Kasia Zagorski*
Editorial Assistant: *Audra Longert*
Production Supervisor: *Mike Burggren*
Marketing Manager: *Jim McDonough*
Manufacturing Manager: *Marcia Locke*
Director, ELL Training and Development: *Evelyn Nelson*
Photography Manager: *Sheri Blaney*
Development: *Proof Positive/Farrowlyne Associates, Inc.*
Design and Production: *Proof Positive/Farrowlyne Associates, Inc.*
Cover Designer: *Studio Montage*
Printer: *Globus Printing Company*

Printed in the United States of America.
1 2 3 4 5 6 7 8 9 10 08 07 06 05 04 03

For more information, contact Heinle, 25 Thomson Place, Boston, Massachusetts 02210 USA, or you can visit our Internet site at http://www.heinle.com

For permission to use material from this text or product contact us:
Tel 1-800-730-2214
Fax 1-800-730-2215
Web www.thomsonrights.com

ISBN: 0-8384-5350-3

Contents

Introduction and Overview

The *Visions* Assessment Program was designed to ensure standards-based accountability for teachers and students alike. It begins with a Diagnostic Test to assess what students already know and to target students' needs in specific skill areas. Throughout the book, students take a Chapter Quiz at the end of each chapter. At the end of each unit, they take a Unit Test. The Assessment Program ensures ongoing as well as summative evaluation with the Mid-Book and End-of-Book Exams. Portfolio Assessment is also taken into account to measure the students' overall progress.

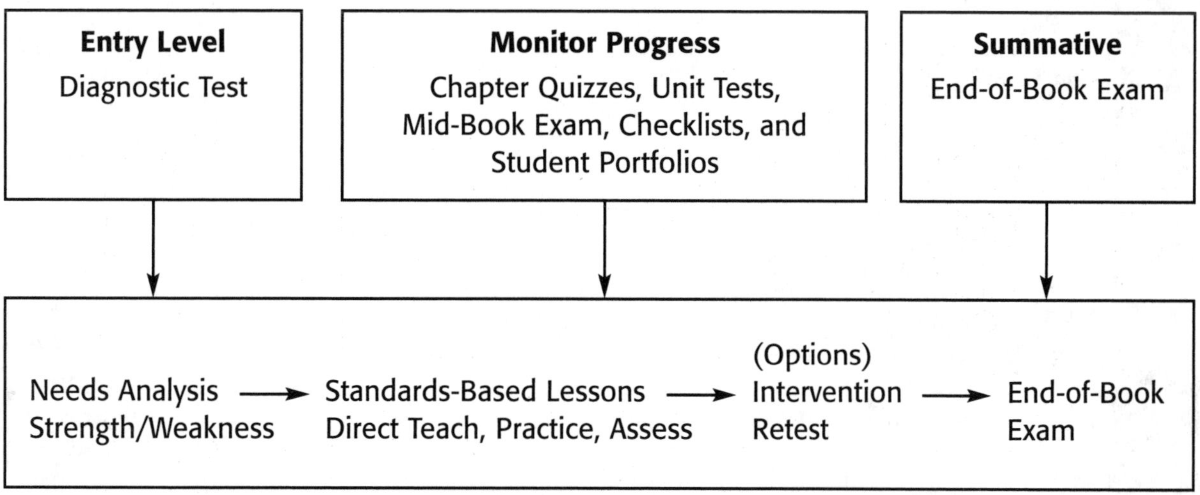

ExamView® is a CD-ROM assessment instrument that allows teachers to create and customize their *Visions* Assessment Program. The Chapter Quizzes, Unit Tests, Mid-Book Exam, and End-of-Book Exam can be customized by adding, deleting, editing, or rearranging questions from the test bank of standards-based assessment items. ***ExamView®*** also allows teachers to create and/or customize tests for the purpose of retesting after intervention.

ENTRY LEVEL PLACEMENT

Heinle recognizes that English Language Learners usually take a placement test such as the *Language Assessment Scales* (LAS), the *California English Language Development Test* (CELDT), the *IDEA Proficiency Test* (IPT), or the Woodcock Muñoz. Heinle provides correlations to these placement tests so teachers know where to place students in the *Visions* program. Contact your local Heinle/Thomson Learning Sales Representative for more information about these correlations.

ASSESSMENT REFERENCE CHART

The reference chart below provides an overview of the assessment instruments, page numbers, and purpose of the assessment tools in the *Visions* Assessment Program.

	Name	Pages	Purpose of Assessment
Entry Level	**Diagnostic Test**	1–6	To enable teachers to ascertain their students' skills in vocabulary, reading, grammar, spelling, and writing, and to perform a Needs Analysis in order to target specific instructional needs.
Monitor Progress	**Chapter Quizzes**	7–96	To monitor students' ongoing progress in vocabulary, grammar, reading, and writing. There are 27 Chapter Quizzes.
	Unit Tests	17–102	To monitor students' ongoing progress toward meeting strategies and standards in vocabulary, grammar, reading, and writing at the end of each unit. There are 6 Unit Tests.
	Mid-Book Exam	55–60	To monitor students' ongoing progress toward meeting strategies and standards in vocabulary, grammar, reading, and writing as taught throughout the first three units of the book.
	Student Resources Checklists	115–133	To promote student responsibility in meeting the standards. Students self-assess their strengths and weaknesses for purposes of reteaching if necessary.
Summative	**End-of-Book Exam**	103–108	To measure students' achievement and mastery in meeting the standards in vocabulary, reading, and writing as taught throughout the book.
Monitor Progress	**Peer Editing** Checklists	117–120	To collaboratively involve classmates in giving and gaining feedback on their progress toward meeting the standards in writing.
	Active Listening Checklist	124	To collaboratively involve classmates in giving and gaining feedback on their progress in the area of listening and speaking during oral presentations.
	Teacher Resources Listening, Speaking, Reading, Writing, Viewing, and Content Area Checklists	134	To track ongoing progress of students in all domains of the standards, and to serve as a vehicle in planning instruction.
	Reading Fluency	116, 136	To check students' progress in learning to read silently and aloud with expression, and to adjust their reading rates according to the purpose of their reading.
	Rubrics	136–137	To evaluate students' overall performance using a fixed measurement scale and a list of criteria taken from formal and informal outcomes. These rubrics should be part of each student's permanent record.
	Portfolio Assessment	115	To involve students in self-reflection on their progress in meeting their learning goals. This ongoing assessment is a collection of student work that exhibits the student's best efforts and progress.
	ExamView® **CD-ROM**	CD-ROM	To empower teachers to choose and customize test items to meet students' targeted needs; items chosen may be used to retest after intervention activities.

ENTRY LEVEL

DIAGNOSTIC TEST

The following subtests appear in the Diagnostic Test. These subtests may be taken all at once or at multiple diagnostic sessions.

A. **Vocabulary Meaning Subtest** This subtest assesses the learner's vocabulary and ability to derive meaning from context. The ability to comprehend and read contextually is an indispensable skill, just as successful contextual reading requires an adequate vocabulary.

B. **Word Study Subtest** This subtest assesses the learner's ability to recognize parts of words (such as suffixes, prefixes, and roots) and to sound out words. It also assesses the dictionary skills covered in each level of *Visions* that pertain to word analysis.

C. **Reading Comprehension Subtest** This subtest evaluates the learner's ability to answer questions about a silently-read passage. The learner's reading rate (fluency) may also be measured in addition to his/her understanding of the reading.

D. **Reading Strategies Subtest** This subtest assesses the successful use of various reading strategies presented in *Visions.*

E. **Grammar/Usage Subtest** This subtest evaluates skills that match the standards taken from the Grammar Focus section of *Visions.*

F. **Spelling Subtest** This subtest assesses the learner's spelling skills. It mirrors the spelling skills found in the Writing section of the *Visions* Activity Book.

G. **Writing Subtest** This subtest assesses the learner's writing skills. Skills from this section mirror the writing practice given in *Visions.* Learners are asked to write in sentences.

H. **Writing Conventions Subtest** This subtest assesses the learner's capitalization and punctuation skills. Students must identify mistakes using a multiple-choice format.

MONITORING PROGRESS

CHAPTER QUIZZES

Each chapter has a two-page quiz with 20 multiple-choice questions and one writing prompt. The following subtests within the Chapter Quizzes reflect the skills that have been taught in the various sections of each chapter. A scoring guide has been included to ensure consistency and fairness.

A. Vocabulary (based on the Build Vocabulary and Word Study sections of the chapter)

B. **Text Structure/Elements of Literature**

C. **Reading Strategies**

D. **Grammar/Usage**

E. **Writing**

UNIT TESTS

Each unit has a six-page test with 40 multiple-choice questions and one writing prompt. There are nine subtests within the Unit Tests. Each subtest reflects the skills within the unit and the skills found on state tests. A scoring guide has been included to ensure consistency and fairness. The nine subtests are as follows:

A. **Reading** Allows students to apply and assess the skills they have learned in the unit.

B. **Reading Comprehension** Assesses literal, inferential, and higher-order thinking through multiple-choice questions.

C. **Reading Strategies** Assesses skills emphasized in Standards Assessment, such as identifying main idea/details, making inferences, drawing conclusions, and so on.

D. **Elements of Literature** Assesses knowledge of literary elements emphasized in Standards Assessment, such as plot, setting, character, point of view, and so on.

E. **Vocabulary** Assesses vocabulary skills emphasized in Standards Assessment, such as prefixes, suffixes, root words, and so on.

F. **Grammar/Usage** Assesses knowledge and skills emphasized in grammar and usage Standards Assessment.

G. **Editing** Assesses students' ability to identify problems in writing and to correct or improve them.

H. Writing Conventions Assesses knowledge and application of spelling, capitalization, and punctuation.

I. Writing Assesses students' writing skills. The writing prompt is centered on the unit theme. Planning guidelines or tips are included to help students write.

SUMMATIVE EVALUATION

MID-BOOK AND END-OF-BOOK EXAMS

Mid-Book Exam Assesses skills covered in *Visions,* Units 1–3.

End-of-Book Exam Assesses skills covered in *Visions,* Units 1–6.

Both exams reflect the type and nature of testing done on standardized tests. They help prepare students to take language arts and English language-learner types of tests. The nine subtests within each Mid-Book and End-of-Book Exam are the same as the Unit subtests but require more higher-order thinking. Students are required to write a three-paragraph essay in *Visions* A and a five-paragraph essay in *Visions* B & C.

STUDENT RESOURCES

PORTFOLIO ASSESSMENT

Introducing the portfolio

Distribute a folder to each student in the class. Direct students to write their names on their portfolios and make a design, such as a coat-of-arms, that pictorially tells something about them. Write the word *portfolio* on the board and explain that their portfolio is a collection of their best work. At least one piece of their work from each unit should go into their portfolio. Their portfolios should contain the best examples of the effort, progress, and achievements they have made throughout *Visions.*

Student participation in selecting pieces

Students should save all of the work they do in each unit in a "work" folder. At the end of each unit, students will select their best work from this collection to add to their portfolio. Model the portfolio selection process by distributing the *Portfolio: Activity Rating and Reflection Sheet* (p. 115). Then, write on the board: "What is the piece or activity I liked the most?" Demonstrate removing the selected piece from their work folder and placing it in the portfolio.

Discuss the criteria for selecting pieces

Discuss with the class the reasons for making a portfolio selection. Add their responses to a list on the board. Be sure to explain to students the following characteristics of a portfolio:

- **It is continuous and ongoing.** A portfolio contains samples of work that stretch over an entire marking period and can be accompanied by art, videotapes, and computer graphics.
- **It provides for student reflection** about students' own work and learning.
- **It contains a variety of different assessment tools** including student checklists.

Paulson, F.L., Paulson, P.R., and Meyer, CA. (1991, February). "What Makes a Portfolio a Portfolio?" *Educational Leadership,* pp. 60–63.

Portfolio: Activity Rating and Reflection Sheet

Show students how to fill out the *Portfolio: Activity Rating and Reflection Sheet.* Have students work with a partner to share their work and discuss their responses before completing the sheet. When students have completed the sheet, have them attach it to the piece that they select to place in their portfolio.

Completing the portfolio process

Explain where students should put their portfolios for storage until the next time they use them. Also explain where students should keep their "work" folders. The pieces of work gathered from the unit that were not selected to include in the portfolio may be taken home.

READING FLUENCY

Practice

Throughout *Visions,* students receive practice in all the basic subskills of reading fluency.

Each lesson is designed to cover and scaffold fluency instruction for English language learners. The subskills include word recognition, chunking, phrases, oral reading, silent reading, reading comprehension, adjusting rate for purpose, repeated reading, and reading with expression.

The Reading Fluency Chart (p. 116) serves two assessment purposes. It serves as a record for:

1. The number of words per minute a student reads aloud.
2. The number of words per minute a student reads silently.

After students have recorded their progress on their Reading Fluency Charts, the students' grade level in reading fluency can be determined by referring to the rubric below.

Average rates for reading for students in Grades 2–12

Grade Equivalent	Standard Words per Minute
2.5	121
3.5	135
4.5	149
5.5	163
6.5	177
7.5	191
8.5	205
9.5	219
10.5	233
11.5	247
12.5	261

Source: Carver (1990)
National Center for Education Statistics

CHECKLISTS

Student Checklists are an integral part of the portfolio evaluation process. They provide feedback and a record of student progress in listening, speaking, reading, writing, and viewing. These checklists are referenced in the *Visions* Teacher Editions and are reproducible from the Assessment Program. The checklists and evaluation forms provided are:

TEACHER RESOURCES

CHECKLISTS

The Teacher Resource reproducible checklists should be used to plan and evaluate instruction. The *Lesson Plan Checklist for The Sheltered Instruction Observation Protocol* (*SIOP*) (pp. 134–135) can be used during the Across Content Areas sections of *Visions.* The *Rubric for Oral Reading Fluency* (p. 136) will help you assess the progress of your students during the Build Reading Fluency sections of the student book. You may want to give students a copy of the *Rubric for Oral Presentations* (p. 137) that you will use for grading. The following important checklists serve as a guideline for standards-based accountability. Four marking periods are provided for each standard.

- Listening and Speaking Standards Assessment Checklist, pp. 138–139
- Reading Standards Assessment Checklist, pp. 140–141
- Writing Standards Assessment Checklist, pp. 142–143
- Viewing and Representing Standards Assessment Checklist, p. 144

Name ______________________ Date ______________________

Answer Sheet

For Diagnostic Test, Unit Tests, Mid-Book Exam, and End-of-Book Exam

Fill in the circles of the correct answers. Erase mistakes well.

☐ **Diagnostic Test**

☐ **Unit ____ Test**

☐ **Mid-Book Exam**

☐ **End-of-Book Exam**

1. ⓐ ⓑ ⓒ ⓓ	**11.** ⓐ ⓑ ⓒ ⓓ	**21.** ⓐ ⓑ ⓒ ⓓ	**31.** ⓐ ⓑ ⓒ ⓓ
2. ⓐ ⓑ ⓒ ⓓ	**12.** ⓐ ⓑ ⓒ ⓓ	**22.** ⓐ ⓑ ⓒ ⓓ	**32.** ⓐ ⓑ ⓒ ⓓ
3. ⓐ ⓑ ⓒ ⓓ	**13.** ⓐ ⓑ ⓒ ⓓ	**23.** ⓐ ⓑ ⓒ ⓓ	**33.** ⓐ ⓑ ⓒ ⓓ
4. ⓐ ⓑ ⓒ ⓓ	**14.** ⓐ ⓑ ⓒ ⓓ	**24.** ⓐ ⓑ ⓒ ⓓ	**34.** ⓐ ⓑ ⓒ ⓓ
5. ⓐ ⓑ ⓒ ⓓ	**15.** ⓐ ⓑ ⓒ ⓓ	**25.** ⓐ ⓑ ⓒ ⓓ	**35.** ⓐ ⓑ ⓒ ⓓ
6. ⓐ ⓑ ⓒ ⓓ	**16.** ⓐ ⓑ ⓒ ⓓ	**26.** ⓐ ⓑ ⓒ ⓓ	**36.** ⓐ ⓑ ⓒ ⓓ
7. ⓐ ⓑ ⓒ ⓓ	**17.** ⓐ ⓑ ⓒ ⓓ	**27.** ⓐ ⓑ ⓒ ⓓ	**37.** ⓐ ⓑ ⓒ ⓓ
8. ⓐ ⓑ ⓒ ⓓ	**18.** ⓐ ⓑ ⓒ ⓓ	**28.** ⓐ ⓑ ⓒ ⓓ	**38.** ⓐ ⓑ ⓒ ⓓ
9. ⓐ ⓑ ⓒ ⓓ	**19.** ⓐ ⓑ ⓒ ⓓ	**29.** ⓐ ⓑ ⓒ ⓓ	**39.** ⓐ ⓑ ⓒ ⓓ
10. ⓐ ⓑ ⓒ ⓓ	**20.** ⓐ ⓑ ⓒ ⓓ	**30.** ⓐ ⓑ ⓒ ⓓ	**40.** ⓐ ⓑ ⓒ ⓓ

Name ______________________ Date ______________________

Answer Sheet

For Chapter Quizzes

Fill in the circles of the correct answers. Erase mistakes well.

Chapter ____ Quiz

1. ⓐ ⓑ ⓒ ⓓ	**11.** ⓐ ⓑ ⓒ ⓓ
2. ⓐ ⓑ ⓒ ⓓ	**12.** ⓐ ⓑ ⓒ ⓓ
3. ⓐ ⓑ ⓒ ⓓ	**13.** ⓐ ⓑ ⓒ ⓓ
4. ⓐ ⓑ ⓒ ⓓ	**14.** ⓐ ⓑ ⓒ ⓓ
5. ⓐ ⓑ ⓒ ⓓ	**15.** ⓐ ⓑ ⓒ ⓓ
6. ⓐ ⓑ ⓒ ⓓ	**16.** ⓐ ⓑ ⓒ ⓓ
7. ⓐ ⓑ ⓒ ⓓ	**17.** ⓐ ⓑ ⓒ ⓓ
8. ⓐ ⓑ ⓒ ⓓ	**18.** ⓐ ⓑ ⓒ ⓓ
9. ⓐ ⓑ ⓒ ⓓ	**19.** ⓐ ⓑ ⓒ ⓓ
10. ⓐ ⓑ ⓒ ⓓ	**20.** ⓐ ⓑ ⓒ ⓓ

Diagnostic Test Results Chart

Record students' scores for each section of the diagnostic test here.

Student Name	**A.** Vocabulary Meaning	**B.** Word Study	**C.** Reading Comprehension	**D.** Reading Strategies	**E.** Grammar/ Usage	**F.** Spelling	**G.** Writing	**H.** Writing Conventions
1.								
2.								
3.								
4.								
5.								
6.								
7.								
8.								
9.								
10.								
11.								
12.								
13.								
14.								
15.								
16.								
17.								

Intervention/Reteaching Component Guide

This chart serves as a guide to the *Visions* components you can use to reteach the skills tested on the Unit Tests, the Mid-Book Exam, and the End-of-Book Exam.

	Student Book	Teacher Edition	Activity Book	Student Handbook	Student CD-ROM	More Grammar Practice workbook	Teacher Resource Book
A. Reading Comprehension	X	X			X		
B. Reading Strategies	X	X		X	X		X
C. Elements of Literature	X	X	X	X	X		
D. Vocabulary	X		X	X	X		X
E. Grammar/ Usage	X		X	X	X	X	
F. Editing				X			
G. Writing Conventions		X	X	X	X		
H. Writing	X		X	X			X

Student Name ______________________

Individual Progress Chart for Intervention

Chapter Quizzes

The purpose of this chart is to record the student's progress and to use it as a basis for intervention and reteaching. Note sub-sections of the quizzes where the student is weak and target those areas as part of the intervention plan.

Formal Assessment

Record the student's scores for each sub-section of the quizzes.
Write the number correct over the number of possible points for each sub-section.

	Unit 1					Unit 2					Unit 3					Unit 4				Unit 5				Unit 6			
	1	2	3	4	5	1	2	3	4	5	1	2	3	4	5	1	2	3	4	1	2	3	4	1	2	3	4
A. Vocabulary	/	/	/	/	/	/	/	/	/	/	/	/	/	/	/	/	/	/	/	/	/	/	/	/	/	/	/
B. Text Structure/ Elements of Literature	/	/	/	/	/	/	/	/	/	/	/	/	/	/	/	/	/	/	/	/	/	/	/	/	/	/	/
C. Reading Strategies	/	/	/	/	/	/	/	/	/	/	/	/	/	/	/	/	/	/	/	/	/	/	/	/	/	/	/
D. Grammar/ Usage	/	/	/	/	/	/	/	/	/	/	/	/	/	/	/	/	/	/	/	/	/	/	/	/	/	/	/
E. Writing	/	/	/	/	/	/	/	/	/	/	/	/	/	/	/	/	/	/	/	/	/	/	/	/	/	/	/

Student Name ___________________________

Individual Progress Chart for Intervention

Unit Tests, Mid-Book Exam, End-of-Book Exam

The purpose of this chart is to record the student's progress and to use it as a basis for intervention and reteaching. Note sub-sections of the tests where the student is weak and target those areas as part of the intervention plan.

Formal Assessment

Write the number correct over the number of possible points for each sub-section.

	Unit 1 Test	Unit 2 Test	Unit 3 Test	Mid-Book Exam	Unit 4 Test	Unit 5 Test	Unit 6 Test	End-of-Book Exam
Reading Comprehension	/20	/20	/20	/20	/20	/20	/20	/20
Reading Strategies	/10	/10	/10	/10	/10	/10	/10	/10
Elements of Literature	/10	/10	/10	/10	/10	/10	/10	/10
Vocabulary	/10	/10	/10	/10	/10	/10	/10	/10
Grammar/Usage	/10	/10	/10	/10	/10	/10	/10	/10
Editing	/10	/10	/10	/10	/10	/10	/10	/10
Writing Conventions	/10	/10	/10	/10	/10	/10	/10	/10
Writing	/20	/20	/20	/20	/20	/20	/20	/20

Authentic Assessment

Record your observations of the student's strengths and needs.

Student Portfolio	Teacher Observation (language development, content, organization, creativity, other)
Unit 1	
Unit 2	
Unit 3	
Unit 4	
Unit 5	
Unit 6	

Interpersonal Skills	Teacher Observation (participation, cooperation, other)
Unit 1	
Unit 2	
Unit 3	
Unit 4	
Unit 5	
Unit 6	

Holistic Scoring Guide for Writing Assessment

	20 points	15 points	10 points	5 points
Development of Ideas Are ideas presented and supported insightfully?	• Ideas are thoroughly developed. • Development reflects thought. • Ideas are presented insightfully. • Compositional risks enhance writing.	• Ideas are reasonably well-developed. • Development shows thought. • Ideas show thought. • Few compositional risks evident.	• Idea development is attempted. • Omitted information creates minor gaps between ideas.	• Little or no idea development is evident. • Ideas are a summary of a known writing, movie, or TV show. • Omitted information creates significant gaps between ideas.
Organization Are ideas ordered logically from sentence to paragraph?	• Thought progression is smooth and controlled. • Transitions are meaningful. • Order of ideas is logical. • Organizational strategies enhance presentation of ideas.	• Thought progression is generally smooth and controlled. • Transitions are mostly meaningful. • Ideas are mostly linked. • Effective organizational strategies. • Minor wordiness and/or repetition.	• Thought progression is somewhat smooth and logical. • More transitions are needed. • Ideas are somewhat linked. • Ineffective organizational strategy. • Some wordiness and/or repetition.	• Progression of thought is not logical. • Inappropriate use or lack of transitions. • There is no organizational strategy. • Wordiness and/or repetition inhibits progression of ideas.
Voice Does the writer engage the reader and express his/her individuality?	• Reader is engaged throughout. • Composition sounds original. • Individuality and unique voice are expressed.	• Reader is generally engaged. • In general, composition sounds original. • Writing generally expresses individuality.	• Reader is engaged sporadically. • Parts of the composition sound original. • Writing expresses some individuality.	• Writing does not engage the reader. • Little or no sense of the writer's voice. • Composition does not sound original. • Writing does not express individuality.
Fluency and Focus How well do individual paragraphs and the whole composition flow together?	• Focus is sustained throughout. • Writing has sense of completeness. • Introduction/conclusion are meaningful. • All/most of writing contributes to development and quality.	• Writing is generally focused. • Clear relationship between ideas. • Few sudden shifts in ideas. • Overall sense of completeness. • Introduction/conclusion add depth. • Most of writing contributes to development and quality.	• Writing is somewhat focused. • Writer shifts ideas, but ideas are related. • Some sense of completeness. • Introduction/conclusion are superficial. • Some of writing is extraneous.	• Writing is not focused. • Writer shifts ideas abruptly. • Little or no sense of completeness. • Introduction/conclusion are inadequate. • Much of writing is extraneous. • Connection to prompt is weak.
Conventions Are spelling, capitalization, punctuation, grammar, usage, and sentence structure appropriate?	• Writing shows a strong/consistent command of conventions. • Minor errors occur during compositional risks. • Words, phrases, and sentence structure enhance effectiveness.	• Writing shows good command of conventions. • Minor errors do not disrupt fluency. • Words, phrases, and sentence structure are generally appropriate and contribute to effectiveness.	• Writing shows limited control of conventions. • Errors weaken fluency. • Simple or inaccurate words and phrases and awkward sentences limit effectiveness.	• Writing has severe/frequent errors in conventions. • There is an overall lack of fluency. • There is frequent misuse/omission of words and phrases. • Frequent use of awkward sentences.
Presentation Does format ease and enhance understanding?	• Penmanship is pleasing. • Margins and spacing enhance understanding. • Devices (headings, bullets, numbers, etc.) clarify and organize information.	• Penmanship is clear. • Margins and spacing are appropriate. • Devices (headings, bullets, numbers, etc.) are somewhat effective.	• Penmanship is difficult to interpret. • Margins and spacing are inconsistent. • Devices (headings, bullets, numbers, etc.) are superficial.	• Penmanship is illegible. • Margins and spacing are confusing. • Inappropriate use or lack of devices (headings, bullets, numbers, etc.).

Name ______________________ Date ______________ Grade

DIAGNOSTIC TEST

A. ➤ Vocabulary Meaning: Choose the correct answer. *(10 points)*

1. _____ stories are often about unsolved crimes.
a. Humorous
b. Happy
c. Mystery
d. Adventure

2. How are these words related? ***astronaut, orbit, gravity***
a. They are about cities.
b. They are about space.
c. They are about food.
d. They are about water.

3. ***Ancient*** and ***ancestor*** refer to something that is _____.
a. old
b. large
c. small
d. beautiful

4. Ana adores peanut butter. She eats it every day. ***Adores*** means _____.
a. misses
b. likes a little
c. likes a lot
d. doesn't like

5. The peak of the mountain is 3 miles high. ***Peak*** means _____.
a. bottom
b. top
c. under
d. back

B. ➤ Word Study: Choose the correct answer. *(10 points)*

6. What two words make up the compound word ***snowflake***?
a. sno + wflake
b. snow + flake
c. snowf + lake
d. snowfla + ke

7. The word ***heartless*** means *without a heart.* The word ***thoughtless*** means _____.
a. thinking
b. full of heart
c. with heart
d. without thought

8. Which word has the same beginning sound as ***thank***?
a. tank
b. hand
c. think
d. Hank

9. The study of ***biology*** is part of _____.
a. music
b. science
c. social studies
d. math

10. The opposite of *over* is _____.
a. out
b. up
c. over
d. under

Name ______________________ Date ______________________

DIAGNOSTIC TEST *(continued)*

C. ➤ Reading Comprehension: Choose the correct answer based on the readings. *(20 points)*

The Iditarod

1 Every year in early March, dogs pull sleds in a race along the Iditarod Trail. This trail is 1770 kilometers long. It goes from Anchorage to Nome, Alaska. The people who drive the dog teams are called mushers.

2 A musher is an adventurer. He runs by himself with his dogs. Some mushers are women. Susan Butcher is a famous musher. She won the Iditarod race four times. Rick Swenson won the race five times.

3 Mushers are very brave to go on this adventure. The dogs run across snow and ice pulling their sleds. Sometimes the mushers ride, and sometimes they walk. In 1991, Rick Swenson led his dogs through a snowstorm. It was so dark that no one could see. In 1990, Susan Butcher's dogs got sick.

4 At night, the mushers sleep in tents. In the morning, they can see footprints of wild animals near the camp. Sometimes they have to scare the wild animals to make them go away.

5 The Iditarod race is very long, dangerous, and cold. The mushers spend eleven or twelve days running this race. The temperature can go down to –46 degrees C (minus forty-six degrees Celsius). The dogs and the mushers take care of each other during this adventure.

11. A musher ____.
- **a.** is a dog
- **b.** drives a dog team
- **c.** hates animals
- **d.** doesn't use a sled

12. A person can win the race ____.
- **a.** one time
- **b.** four times
- **c.** many times
- **d.** five times

13. How long is the Iditarod Trail?
- **a.** five times
- **b.** 1990
- **c.** 1770 kilometers
- **d.** –46 degrees Celsius

14. Iditarod is the name of a ____.
- **a.** musher
- **b.** dog
- **c.** trail
- **d.** girl

15. What dangers do the dogs face?
- **a.** heat
- **b.** mushers
- **c.** footprints
- **d.** snowstorms

Name ______________________________ Date ______________________

DIAGNOSTIC TEST (continued)

The Man, the Boy, and the Donkey, by Aesop

1 A man and his son were going with their donkey to the market. As they were walking along, a man passed them and said: "You fools, why don't you ride upon your donkey?"

2 So the man put the boy on the donkey and they went on their way. Soon they passed a group of men. One of the men said: "See that lazy child. He lets his father walk while he rides."

3 So the man ordered the boy to get off, and he got on himself. But they hadn't gone far when they passed two women. One woman said to the other: "Shame on that lazy man to let his poor little son walk."

4 Well, the man didn't know what to do. At last he took his boy up before him on the donkey. By this time they had come to the town. The people began to yell and point at them. The man stopped and asked what they were pointing at. The people said: "Aren't you ashamed of yourself for overloading your poor donkey?"

5 The man and boy got off and tried to think what to do. They thought and thought. At last, they tied the donkey's feet to a pole, and raised the pole and donkey to their shoulders. They carried the donkey along until they came to Market Bridge. The donkey got one of his feet loose, kicked, and caused the boy to drop his end of the pole. The donkey fell over the bridge. His other feet were still tied together, so he drowned.

6 "That will teach you," said an old man who had followed them: "Try to please everyone and you will please no one."

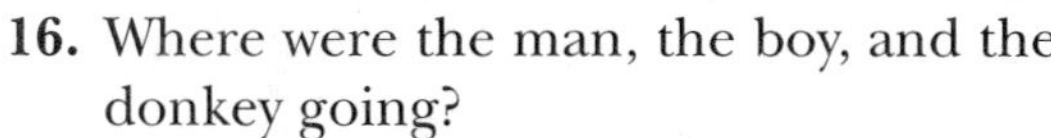

16. Where were the man, the boy, and the donkey going?
- **a.** to the bridge
- **b.** to the market
- **c.** to the country
- **d.** for a walk

17. Who put the boy on the donkey?
- **a.** the man
- **b.** the boy
- **c.** the donkey
- **d.** no one rode the donkey

18. Who did the man pass while riding on his donkey?
- **a.** the man
- **b.** two women
- **c.** the donkey
- **d.** the boy

19. Who yelled and pointed at the man and the boy?
- **a.** the donkey
- **b.** the son
- **c.** the people
- **d.** the child

20. Who fell over the bridge into the water?
- **a.** the man
- **b.** the boy
- **c.** the donkey
- **d.** no one

Name ______________________________ Date ____________________

DIAGNOSTIC TEST *(continued)*

D. ➤ Reading Strategies: Choose the correct answer. *(10 points)*

21. What can you infer about mushers from *The Iditarod*?
- **a.** They like a challenge.
- **b.** They like footprints.
- **c.** They like tents.
- **d.** They like to skate.

22. What is the main idea of the reading, *The Iditarod*?
- **a.** The Iditarod is in March.
- **b.** Wild animals are dangerous.
- **c.** The Iditarod is an exciting and a dangerous race.
- **d.** Rick Swenson was in a snowstorm.

23. Who is the author of *The Man, the Boy, and the Donkey*?
- **a.** the Donkey
- **b.** the Man
- **c.** Aesop
- **d.** the Man, the Boy, and the Donkey

24. What is the moral of *The Man, the Boy, and the Donkey*?
- **a.** "If you try to please everyone, you will please no one."
- **b.** "Shame on that lazy man to let his poor little son walk."
- **c.** The Man, the Boy, and the Donkey
- **d.** "Aren't you ashamed of yourself for overloading your poor donkey?"

25. What caused the donkey to drown?
- **a.** the boy fell
- **b.** the man thought
- **c.** the feet of the donkey were tied
- **d.** the donkey kicked

Name ______________________ Date ______________

DIAGNOSTIC TEST (continued)

E. ➤ Grammar/Usage: Choose the correct answer. *(10 points)*

26. My brother ____ me to school every day.
- **a.** drive
- **b.** drives
- **c.** ride
- **d.** run

27. We ____ at lunch when the fire alarm rang.
- **a.** be
- **b.** is
- **c.** was
- **d.** were

28. My name is Rita. I am ____ Texas.
- **a.** of
- **b.** on
- **c.** from
- **d.** at

29. Maria is wet because she was ____.
- **a.** swim
- **b.** swimmer
- **c.** swimming
- **d.** swam

30. Carlos wants to play baseball, ____ he must study first.
- **a.** and
- **b.** because
- **c.** but
- **d.** also

F. ➤ Spelling: Choose the correct answer. *(10 points)*

31. The Iditarod is an exciting race. ____ an adventure.
- **a.** It
- **b.** Is
- **c.** Its
- **d.** It's

32. Which pair of words rhyme?
- **a.** give/alive
- **b.** men/mean
- **c.** tale/rail
- **d.** four/hour

33. We ____ our jackets before we went out into the cold.
- **a.** button
- **b.** butoned
- **c.** buttoned
- **d.** butund

34. The book on the table is ____.
- **a.** yurs
- **b.** yers
- **c.** yours
- **d.** ures

35. ____ are interesting animals.
- **a.** Wulfs
- **b.** Wolfs
- **c.** Wolves
- **d.** Wulf

Name ______________________ Date ______________________

DIAGNOSTIC TEST *(continued)*

G. ➤ Writing: Write a paragraph about the topic below. Write your paragraph on a piece of paper. *(20 points)*

> **Writing Prompt** Write a paragraph about something that you like to do, for example, a game, a hobby, or an activity. Describe what it is and give instructions how to do it.

H. ➤ Writing Conventions: There is one mistake in each sentence. Choose the letter that is under the mistake. *(10 points)*

36. People from all over the united States like
a b c
to listen to stories.
d

37. Does your family have a tradition of
a b c
storytelling.
d

38. We tell stories on Holidays, like
a b
Independence Day.
c d

39. we listen to the stories and then we laugh
a b c
together.
d

40. "Traditions are important to a family,"
a b c
says my "mother".
d

Name ______________________________ Date ______________ Grade

QUIZ Unit 1 • Chapter 1

A. ➤ Vocabulary: Choose the correct answer. *(24 points: 4 points each)*

1. A reader can use language structure to _____.
   - **a.** make the text interesting
   - **b.** learn how to read
   - **c.** build a story
   - **d.** figure out what a word means

2. Lena hunted for her hat. She could not find it. Hunted means _____.
   - **a.** hid
   - **b.** looked
   - **c.** put on
   - **d.** took off

3. Fahad detests broccoli. He never eats it. Detests means _____.
   - **a.** loves
   - **b.** hates
   - **c.** sees
   - **d.** likes

4. A compound word _____.
   - **a.** brings two sentences together
   - **b.** uses a comma between two words
   - **c.** has two words that are joined together
   - **d.** makes words shorter

5. Which is a compound word?
   - **a.** doorknob
   - **b.** marker
   - **c.** don't
   - **d.** happily

6. Which is a compound word?
   - **a.** singing
   - **b.** rewrite
   - **c.** sidewalk
   - **d.** joyfully

B. ➤ Text Structure/Elements of Literature: Read and choose the correct answer. *(32 points: 4 points each)*

> "Amazing Bats"
>
> 1 Bats are amazing. They are the only mammals that can fly. Mammals are warm-blooded animals. Female mammals feed milk to their young. The largest bat wings can spread to six feet. Bats rest during the day and hunt for insects at night. Bats are nature's best form of bug control.

7. "Amazing Bats" is a(n)
   - **a.** short story
   - **b.** fairytale
   - **c.** personal narrative
   - **d.** informational text

8. "Amazing Bats" gives _____ about bats.
   - **a.** facts
   - **b.** made-up stories
   - **c.** myths
   - **d.** rhymes

9. When do bats hunt for food?
   - **a.** during the day
   - **b.** at night
   - **c.** over the weekend
   - **d.** in the summer

10. _____ refer to the many different ways writers express themselves.
    - **a.** Definitions
    - **b.** Explanations
    - **c.** Multiple meanings
    - **d.** Elements of literature

11. In stories, visuals are _____.
    - **a.** words
    - **b.** pictures
    - **c.** sentences
    - **d.** paragraphs

Name ______________________________ Date ____________________

QUIZ Unit 1 • Chapter 1 *(continued)*

12. Which visual would help you to picture "Amazing Bats"?
    a. a picture of a farmhouse
    b. a picture of insects
    c. a picture of a bat
    d. a chart of mammals

13. Which visual would help you to picture the bats' eating habits?
    a. a picture of bats during the day
    b. a picture of bats searching for food at night
    c. a picture of insects
    d. a picture of birds flying

14. What is this story mostly about?
    a. why bats like the dark
    b. how bats learn to fly
    c. when bats were discovered
    d. why bats are amazing

C. ➤ Reading Strategies: Choose the correct answer. *(12 points: 4 points each)*

15. ____ is using information that you know to make a guess.
    a. Making inferences
    b. Writing dialogue
    c. Creating sentences
    d. Summarizing stories

16. The boy put on his swimming suit and grabbed a towel. What inference can you make?
    a. The boy is going to school.
    b. The boy is going swimming.
    c. The boy is going to eat.
    d. The boy is going dancing

17. Mr. and Mrs. Ramirez packed their clothes in their suitcases. What inference can you make?
    a. They are going to a movie.
    b. They are going to a restaurant.
    c. They are going on a trip.
    d. They are going to work.

D. ➤ Grammar/Usage: Choose the correct answer. *(12 points: 4 points each)*

18. A part of speech used to connect words in a sentence is a(n) ____.
    a. adjective
    b. interjection
    c. preposition
    d. conjunction

19. Linda tried to call her sister. The line was busy. Which is the best way to combine these sentences?
    a. Linda tried to call her sister, or the line was busy.
    b. Linda tried to call her sister, since the line was busy.
    c. Linda tried to call her sister, but the line was busy.
    d. Linda tried to call her sister, so the line was busy.

20. Lisa wanted to go outside. It was raining. Which is the best way to combine these sentences?
    a. Lisa wanted to go outside, but it was raining.
    b. Lisa wanted to go outside, or it was raining.
    c. Lisa wanted to go outside, for it was raining.
    d. Lisa wanted to go outside, so it was raining.

E. ➤ Writing *(20 points)*

Writing Prompt Write an informational paragraph to describe your favorite animal. Use facts to describe your animal.

VISIONS QUIZ Unit 1 • Chapter 1

Name ______________________________ Date ______________ Grade

QUIZ Unit 1 • Chapter 2

A. ➤ Vocabulary: Choose the correct answer. *(24 points: 4 points each)*

1. Where can you find the meaning of a word?
- **a.** in a title
- **b.** in a dictionary
- **c.** on a map
- **d.** on a timeline

2. The farmland produced good crops. Farmland means _____.
- **a.** land used to grow food
- **b.** a place where animals live
- **c.** land used as a playground
- **d.** a place where sports are viewed

3. Pilar had to change clothes after she fell in the mud. Mud is a mixture of _____.
- **a.** dirt and salt
- **b.** oil and water
- **c.** dirt and water
- **d.** oil and paint

4. A group of letters added to the end of a word is a _____.
- **a.** noun
- **b.** verb
- **c.** prefix
- **d.** suffix

5. A person who studies biology is a _____.
- **a.** salesperson
- **b.** biologist
- **c.** doctor
- **d.** lawyer

6. The study of the way people lived long ago is called _____.
- **a.** biology
- **b.** geology
- **c.** psychology
- **d.** archaeology

B. ➤ Text Structure/Elements of Literature: Read and choose the correct answer. *(32 points: 4 points each)*

"The African Lion"

1 African lions are wonderful creatures. They are four feet tall. They are eight and a half feet long. Male lions are usually four hundred and fifty pounds. Female lions are usually three hundred pounds. They live in large family groups. In the wild, they usually live between fifteen and eighteen years. One scientist says, "Lions are one of the most wonderful creatures in the world!"

7. "The African Lion" is a(n) _____.
- **a.** informational text
- **b.** autobiography
- **c.** diary
- **d.** short story

8. This text mostly _____.
- **a.** discusses wonderful creatures
- **b.** looks at wild animals
- **c.** describes lions
- **d.** discusses many cats

9. _____ lions are usually four hundred and fifty pounds.
- **a.** Male
- **b.** Female
- **c.** Short
- **d.** Pretty

10. The lions in this text are from _____.
- **a.** Asia
- **b.** Mexico
- **c.** Hawaii
- **d.** Africa

Name ____________________ Date ____________________

QUIZ Unit 1 • Chapter 2 *(continued)*

11. Quotes are the exact words that people ____.
    - a. believe
    - b. see
    - c. read
    - d. say

12. Which of these is an example of a quote in "The African Lion"?
    - a. "Lions are one of the most wonderful creatures in the world!"
    - b. African lions are wonderful creatures.
    - c. They are four feet tall.
    - d. They are eight and a half feet long.

13. Quotation marks are placed ____.
    - a. on top of the quote
    - b. around the quote
    - c. underneath the quote
    - d. away from the quote

14. Quotation marks are a form of ____.
    - a. root word
    - b. cause and effect
    - c. punctuation
    - d. inference

C. ➤ Reading Strategies: Choose the correct answer. *(12 points: 4 points each)*

15. The ____ is the most important idea in a paragraph or text.
    - a. main idea
    - b. last detail
    - c. middle sentence
    - d. first noun

16. ____ give information about the main idea.
    - a. Verbs
    - b. Adjectives
    - c. Supporting details
    - d. Context clues

17. A reader usually finds the most important idea of a paragraph ____.
    - a. in a picture
    - b. on the book cover
    - c. beside the author's name
    - d. in the first sentence

D. ➤ Grammar/Usage: Choose the correct answer. *(12 points: 4 points each)*

18. A preposition is a part of ____.
    - a. imagery
    - b. contrast
    - c. punctuation
    - d. speech

19. I will wait for you in the library. What is the prepositional phrase?
    - a. I will wait
    - b. I will wait for you
    - c. for you
    - d. in the library

20. José left his car in the garage and walked to town. What is the prepostional phrase?
    - a. José left
    - b. left his car
    - c. in the garage
    - d. walked to town

E. ➤ Writing *(20 points)*

Writing Prompt Write an informational paragraph about where you live. Use prepositional phrases.

Name ______________________________ Date ________________ Grade

QUIZ Unit 1 • Chapter 3

A. ➤ Vocabulary: Choose the correct answer. *(24 points: 4 points each)*

1. A word that means the opposite of another word is a(n) _____.
   - a. prefix
   - b. antonym
   - c. allegory
   - d. synonym

2. The word vacant means *empty*. The antonym of vacant is _____.
   - a. full
   - b. pretty
   - c. boring
   - d. nice

3. The word criticize means *to find fault with.* An antonym of criticize is _____.
   - a. to party
   - b. to play
   - c. to praise
   - d. to pause

4. _____ combine two words into a shorter word.
   - a. Prefixes
   - b. Antonyms
   - c. Nouns
   - d. Contractions

5. We're eating lunch together. We're is a combination of which two words?
   - a. we and were
   - b. we and are
   - c. were and have
   - d. were and will

6. It's a beautiful day! It's is a combination of which two words?
   - a. it and should
   - b. is and will
   - c. it and is
   - d. it and was

B. ➤ Text Structure/Elements of Literature: Read and choose the correct answer. *(32 points: 4 points each)*

"The Giant Elephant"

1 Elephants are huge. They weigh 5.5 to 7 tons. They eat between 100 and 1,000 pounds of food a day. They eat grass, trees, shrubs, and fruit. They drink 30 to 50 gallons of water every day.

7. "The Giant Elephant" is a(n) _____.
   - a. poem
   - b. fairytale
   - c. informational text
   - d. autobiography

8. "The Giant Elephant" gives the reader _____.
   - a. facts about elephants
   - b. elephant jokes
   - c. other words that name elephants
   - d. elephant rhyming sentences

9. This informational text is mostly about _____.
   - a. what elephants eat
   - b. how water helps elephants to grow
   - c. how elephants look and what they do
   - d. where elephants live

10. This text tells you that elephants drink 30 to 50 gallons of _____ every day.
    - a. food
    - b. leaves
    - c. shrubs
    - d. water

11. Authors use direct address to speak directly to _____.
    - a. themselves
    - b. writers
    - c. the character
    - d. the reader

Name ______________________ Date ______________

QUIZ Unit 1 • Chapter 3 (continued)

12. Direct address is a ___.
  a. literary device
  b. compound word
  c. prefix
  d. suffix

13. An author using direct address uses the pronoun ___.
  a. you
  b. it
  c. I
  d. they

14. Which sentence is an example of direct address?
  a. Elephants eat trees and shrubs.
  b. Elephants weigh 5.5 to 7 tons.
  c. Elephants are much bigger than you.
  d. Elephants are huge animals.

C. ➤ Reading Strategies: Choose the correct answer. *(12 points: 4 points each)*

15. Compaing a text to your own experience can help you ___.
  a. understand the text
  b. find the main idea
  c. define new words
  d. summarize the text

16. To compare a text to your own experience, you can ask yourself ___
  a. What will I do later?
  b. What do I already know about this topic?
  c. How long is this text?
  d. What will happen next?

17. Felix went out in the rain without an umbrella. What does your experience tell you will happen to Felix?
  a. He will play ball.
  b. He will stay dry.
  c. He will eat outside.
  d. He will get wet.

D. ➤ Grammar/Usage: Choose the correct answer. *(12 points: 4 points each)*

18. Dependent clauses have a subject and a ___.
  a. clause
  b. dialogue
  c. noun
  d. verb

19. Bea decided that she would go to the dance. What is the dependent clause?
  a. Bea decided
  b. Bea decided that
  c. that she would go
  d. that she would go to the dance

20. Josef believes that baseball is the most exciting sport. What is the dependent clause?
  a. Josef believes
  b. Josef believes that
  c. that baseball is the most exciting sport
  d. the most exciting sport

E. ➤ Writing *(20 points)*

Writing Prompt Write an informational paragraph about a normal day at school. Use chronology words such as *first, then, next* and *last* to describe what you do.

Name ______________________________ Date ______________ Grade

QUIZ Unit 1 • Chapter 4

A. ➤ Vocabulary: Choose the correct answer. *(24 points: 4 points each)*

1. Michael bought a ticket for the train. The ticket will _____.
   - **a.** tell Michael where to buy his own train
   - **b.** allow Michael to travel on the train
   - **c.** show a picture of Michael getting on the train
   - **d.** stop the train from leaving without Michael

2. Adela is a passenger on the train. A passenger is someone who _____.
   - **a.** rides a train
   - **b.** plays the piano
   - **c.** writes short stories
   - **d.** works in a store

3. We waited at the _____ for the train to arrive.
   - **a.** train track
   - **b.** train car
   - **c.** train station
   - **d.** train whistle

4. Which word has the same beginning sound as the word think?
   - **a.** turn
   - **b.** tray
   - **c.** took
   - **d.** thanks

5. Which word has the same middle sound as mother?
   - **a.** butter
   - **b.** rather
   - **c.** daughter
   - **d.** watcher

6. Which word has the same ending sound as the name Beth?
   - **a.** touch
   - **b.** match
   - **c.** truth
   - **d.** must

B. ➤ Text Structure/Elements of Literature: Read and choose the correct answer. *(32 points: 4 points each)*

> "The Strange Sound"
>
> 1 Imelda hid her head underneath the covers. She kept hearing a scratching sound. It frightened her. She was too afraid to find out what the noise was. She finally got the courage to go to the back door. She breathed a sigh of relief at what she saw. Her dog, Cocoa, was scratching at the door with his paw. He wanted someone to let him inside the house.

7. "The Strange Sound" is a(n) _____.
   - **a.** fable
   - **b.** poem
   - **c.** mystery
   - **d.** novel

8. A mystery usually contains _____.
   - **a.** a play
   - **b.** suspense
   - **c.** timelines
   - **d.** graphic aids

9. What caused Imelda to hide underneath the covers?
   - **a.** She was happy.
   - **b.** She was hungry.
   - **c.** She was afraid.
   - **d.** She was sleepy.

10. At the end of the story, Imelda discovers that the scratching sound is coming from _____.
    - **a.** her dog
    - **b.** Imelda
    - **c.** a neighbor's house
    - **d.** a friend's dog

Name ______________________ Date ______________________

QUIZ Unit 1 • Chapter 4 (continued)

11. Most mysteries have _____.
    a. compare and contrast sentences
    b. a problem and a resolution
    c. more than one mystery to be solved
    d. instructions on how to solve the mystery

12. In a mystery, a problem is often _____.
    a. the chronology of the mystery
    b. a question that needs to be answered
    c. a supporting detail
    d. the resolution

13. In a mystery, the resolution is _____.
    a. where the mystery happens
    b. the dialogue between the characters
    c. a dream of one of the characters
    d. the solution to a problem

14. Which question shows the problem in this story?
    a. What was making the scratching sound?
    b. Where does Imelda live?
    c. Who is Cocoa?
    d. What time of night is it?

C. ➤ Reading Strategies: Choose the correct answer. *(12 points: 4 points each)*

15. _____ is the order of events in a story.
    a. Main idea
    b. Inference
    c. Chronology
    d. Effect

16. Amina brushed her teeth. Then she went to bed. What did Amina do before she went to bed?
    a. brushed her teeth
    b. took a nap
    c. ate dinner
    d. woke up

17. First Rashid unpacked his lunch. Then he placed a napkin in his lap. Finally, he ate his apple. What did Rashid do after he unpacked his lunch?
    a. threw away his trash
    b. placed a napkin in his lap
    c. ate his apple
    d. played outside

D. ➤ Grammar/Usage: Choose the correct answer. *(12 points: 4 points each)*

18. Luis wants to go swimming, but it is raining outside. This is a _____.
    a. dependent clause
    b. simple sentence
    c. compound sentence
    d. complex sentence

19. I am sure that you will do well on the exam. This is a _____.
    a. dependent clause
    b. simple sentence
    c. compound sentence
    d. complex sentence

20. Lara wants to see that movie. This is a _____.
    a. dependent clause
    b. simple sentence
    c. compound sentence
    d. complex sentence

E. ➤ Writing *(20 points)*

Writing Prompt Write a mystery. Use chronology to show when events happened. Tell how the problem is solved.

Name ______________________________ Date ______________ Grade

QUIZ Unit 1 • Chapter 5

A. ➤ Vocabulary: Choose the correct answer. *(24 points: 4 points each)*

1. The book is over _____.
- **a.** where
- **b.** their
- **c.** they're
- **d.** there

2. Where are Carl and Ming going? _____ going to the store.
- **a.** They
- **b.** Their
- **c.** They're
- **d.** There

3. Lana and Ester have a new dog. _____ dog's name is Pepi.
- **a.** They
- **b.** Their
- **c.** They're
- **d.** There

4. The main part of a word is called the _____.
- **a.** prefix
- **b.** root word
- **c.** suffix
- **d.** ending

5. What is the root word of thoughtless?
- **a.** thought
- **b.** thou
- **c.** ght
- **d.** less

6. A _____ is a group of letters added to the end of a word.
- **a.** prefix
- **b.** contraction
- **c.** suffix
- **d.** clause

B. Text Structure/Elements of Literature: Read and choose the correct answer. *(32 points: 4 points each)*

"The Color of the Leaves"

1 Long ago, two girls named Isabel and Lourdes lived in a small village. They were sisters and best friends. One day, their parents made a big decision. Lourdes would go away to music school each fall. This news greatly upset Isabel. Isabel decided she must keep busy while Lourdes was gone. Quietly, fall tiptoed into the village. Isabel began coloring the leaves of the trees. She continued to color until Lourdes returned home. Today, trees honor Isabel by changing colors in the fall.

7. "The Color of the Leaves" is a _____.
- **a.** legend
- **b.** poem
- **c.** novel
- **d.** mystery

8. When does the story take place?
- **a.** yesterday
- **b.** a long time ago
- **c.** in the near future
- **d.** in the present

9. How might "The Color of the Leaves" become part of an oral tradition?
- **a.** Different people may read the story in a book.
- **b.** Students may learn the story from their teacher.
- **c.** Family members may tell the story to younger family members.
- **d.** The writer of the story may share it with many people.

Name ______________________________ Date ____________________

QUIZ Unit 1 • Chapter 5 (continued)

10. Which event from the story is something that really happens?
    - **a.** Fall likes to tiptoe into villages.
    - **b.** A person colors the leaves of every tree in the fall.
    - **c.** Trees honor a girl named Isabel.
    - **d.** Leaves change colors in the fall.

11. You can conclude that Isabel's coloring of the leaves of every tree is ____.
    - **a.** true
    - **b.** made up
    - **c.** believed by many
    - **d.** a fact

12. What is the setting of "The Color of the Leaves"?
    - **a.** a small village
    - **b.** a large forest
    - **c.** a school
    - **d.** a park

13. Authors use tone to express their opinions about ____.
    - **a.** chronology
    - **b.** characters
    - **c.** conclusions
    - **d.** books

14. The tone in the middle of the story is ____.
    - **a.** funny
    - **b.** sad
    - **c.** cheerful
    - **d.** happy

C. ➤ Reading Strategies: Choose the correct answer. *(12 points: 4 points each)*

15. Imagery helps readers to ____.
    - **a.** draw conclusions
    - **b.** learn new vocabulary
    - **c.** form pictures in their minds
    - **d.** understand the actions of a character

16. He lives in the last red brick building. Which words help you to form an image of the building?
    - **a.** he lives
    - **b.** in the
    - **c.** the last
    - **d.** red brick

17. She stirred the soup in the old, black pot. Which words help you to form an image of the pot?
    - **a.** old, black
    - **b.** the soup
    - **c.** in the
    - **d.** she stirred

D. ➤ Grammar/Usage: Choose the correct answer. *(12 points: 4 points each)*

18. A pronoun can replace a____.
    - **a.** prefix
    - **b.** suffix
    - **c.** verb
    - **d.** noun

19. Rafael is a nice boy. He helps his neighbor. The pronoun he refers to the word ____.
    - **a.** Rafael
    - **b.** nice
    - **c.** boy
    - **d.** neighbor

20. Arid and David are brothers. They look a lot alike. The pronoun they refers to the words ____.
    - **a.** are brothers
    - **b.** Arid and David
    - **c.** they look
    - **d.** a lot alike

E. ➤ Writing *(20 points)*

> **Writing Prompt** Write a legend that explains why something happens. Use pronouns.

Name ______________________ Date ______________ Grade

TEST • Unit 1

A. ➤ Reading

Reflex Reactions

1 During my last exam, the doctor asked me to sit on the examination table. "Now, cross your legs and hang them over the edge of the table," she directed. Then she took a small hammer-like instrument and tapped just below my kneecap. My leg kicked out without my thinking about it. "That knee jerk is called the patellar reflex," she told me.

2 Have you ever wondered why your knee does that? Have you ever wondered why the pupils in our eyes automatically grow larger to help us see in dim light? These are examples of reflex reactions. They happen quickly and without conscious thought. Reflexes help our bodies adjust to changes, even while we're sleeping.

3 Some reflexes happen in muscles. For example, goose bumps on your skin are actually tiny hair-erector muscles responding to cold or fear. Other reflexes help control other parts of the body. When you put food on your tongue, a reflex makes your mouth start to "water." And when your knee jerks, it is your nervous system responding to the hammer-like instrument!

4 So the next time you jerk your hand away from water that is steaming hot, thank your reflexes. They help protect your body.

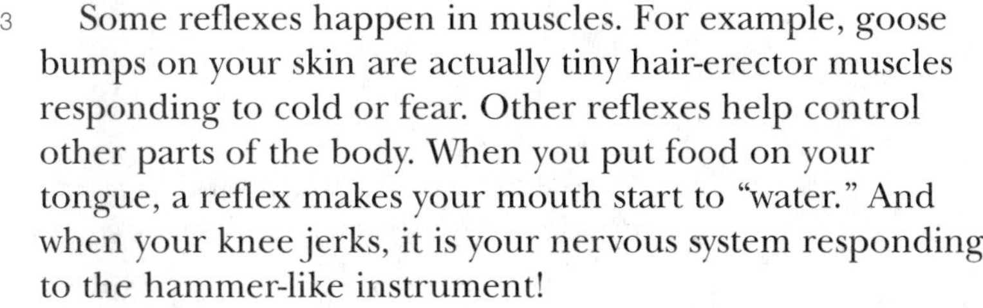

My Notes

Name ______________________ Date ______________________

TEST • Unit 1 *(continued)*

B. ➤ Reading Comprehension: Choose the correct answer. *(20 points: 2 points each)*

1. "Reflex Reactions" is a(n) ____.
   a. novel
   b. short story
   c. interesting legend
   d. informational text

2. The purpose of "Reflex Reactions" is to ____ readers.
   a. entertain
   b. sadden
   c. inform
   d. anger

3. From "Reflex Reactions," you know that your muscles ____.
   a. have reflexes
   b. can hear
   c. have memories
   d. feel pain

4. How does the picture of the knee represent the "Reflex Reactions"?
   a. It shows what a knee looks like when it is broken.
   b. It is one part of the body that does not have reflexes.
   c. It is the body part that the doctor hits with an instrument.
   d. It shows how knees look similar to elbows.

5. What happens to pupils in dim light?
   a. They create tears.
   b. They change colors.
   c. They dry out.
   d. They grow larger.

6. The skin gets goose bumps when it is ____.
   a. hot
   b. cold
   c. new
   d. cracked

7. In the text, what part of the body does the doctor check first?
   a. knee
   b. eyes
   c. head
   d. stomach

8. In paragraph 2, which two body parts respond without conscious thought?
   a. heart and muscle
   b. hair and elbow
   c. knee and eyes
   d. stomach and skin

9. Based on the reading, you can conclude that ____.
   a. the knee is tricky
   b. doctors are interesting people
   c. muscles keep different parts of the body safe
   d. reflexes help to protect the body

10. Where would you most likely find this text?
    a. in a history book
    b. in a science book
    c. in a book of poems
    d. in a book of plays

Name ______________________ Date ______________

TEST • Unit 1 (continued)

C. ➤ Reading Strategies: Choose the correct answer. *(10 points: 2 points each)*

11. In "Reflex Reactions," the writer says that you should thank your reflexes. You can infer that the writer ____.
- **a.** likes to thank different things
- **b.** wonders when is the next time his hand will jerk
- **c.** thinks that people are lucky to have reflexes
- **d.** has never experienced very hot water from a faucet

12. The main idea of paragraph 3 is that ____.
- **a.** there are many types of reflexes
- **b.** goose bumps are a part of the skin
- **c.** reflexes control fear and movement
- **d.** your mouth can be made to "water"

13. Which sentence wants you to use your own experience to understand the text?
- **a.** Some reflexes happen in muscles.
- **b.** Have you wondered why your knee does that?
- **c.** Other reflexes help control other parts of the body.
- **d.** They help protect the body.

14. In "Reflex Reactions," what happens after the writer sits on the table?
- **a.** The speaker kicks out his leg.
- **b.** The speaker thinks about what has just happened.
- **c.** The doctor hits the speaker's knee.
- **d.** The doctor directs the writer to cross his legs.

15. Imagery in "Reflex Reactions" helps you to picture ____.
- **a.** the title of the text
- **b.** pupils in your eyes
- **c.** thanking someone
- **d.** feeling hot water

D. ➤ Elements of Literature: Choose the correct answer. *(10 points: 2 points each)*

16. Which visual would help you to picture the writer's experience with the doctor?
- **a.** a picture of the writer running in the park
- **b.** a chart showing how a muscle flexes
- **c.** a photo of the doctor examining the writer's knee
- **d.** a chart showing the growth of the writer

17. "That knee jerk is called the patellar reflex," she told me. This sentence is an example of ____.
- **a.** choosing the main idea
- **b.** picturing characters in writing
- **c.** using quotes in writing
- **d.** finding the question

18. Have you wondered why the pupils in our eyes automatically grow larger to help us see in dim light? This sentence is an example of ____.
- **a.** problem
- **b.** solution
- **c.** dialogue
- **d.** direct address

19. Which question states the problem discussed in the text?
- **a.** Why does your knee kick out when hit?
- **b.** Who is the writer in the text?
- **c.** How many people use their reflexes each year?
- **d.** How long do reflexes last?

20. What is the tone of "Reflex Reactions"?
- **a.** angry
- **b.** educational
- **c.** disappointed
- **d.** funny

Name ______________________ Date ______________________

E. ➤ Vocabulary: Choose the correct answer. *(10 points: 2 points each)*

21. They help protect your body. In this sentence, your refers to ____.
a. things far away
b. a nearby object
c. something you are going to do
d. something you own

22. It is your nervous system responding. What is the root word of responding?
a. respond
b. ing
c. re
d. pond

23. She tapped just below my kneecap. What is the suffix in the word tapped?
a. *-pp-*
b. *tap-*
c. *-ed*
d. *ta-*

24. Reflexes help our bodies adjust to changes, even while we're sleeping. Which word is a contraction?
a. help
b. our
c. even
d. we're

25. A reflex makes your mouth start to "water." Which is an antonym for the word start?
a. begin
b. end
c. turn
d. go

F. ➤ Grammar/Usage: Choose the correct answer. *(10 points: 2 points each)*

26. Fatima wanted to skate, ____ she had forgotten her roller skates.
a. and
b. or
c. but
d. also

27. Marco sat in his chair after he finished dinner. What is the prepositional phrase?
a. Marco sat
b. in his chair
c. after he finished dinner
d. finished dinner

28. Lee is happy that he did well on the exam. What is the dependent clause?
a. Lee is
b. Lee is happy
c. that he did
d. that he did well on the exam

29. Gabriel creates beautiful pictures. He is an artist. What is the pronoun referent?
a. Gabriel
b. creates
c. beautiful
d. artist

30. Crystal is a great singer and Bailey is a great drummer. This is a ____ sentence.
a. dependent
b. simple
c. complex
d. compound

Name ______________________ Date ______________

TEST • Unit 1 (continued)

G. ➤ Writing Conventions: Choose the correct answer. *(10 points: 2 points each)*

31. Which sentence is correct?
a. Put the cup on the table.
b. Where is Lisa.
c. Look to the left
d. When did you get here,

32. The teacher said, "_____ right."
a. Your
b. You're
c. You is
d. You

33. What is the plural of the word <u>leaf</u>?
a. leave
b. leaf
c. leaves
d. leaft

34. <u>You'll</u> see me soon. What is another way to write <u>you'll</u>?
a. you I'll
b. you would
c. you will
d. you don't

35. This is the _____ chair.
a. babys
b. babies
c. baby's
d. babyes

H. ➤ Editing *(10 points: 2 points each)*

(1) Lisa wanted to stay awake. (2) Her was getting sleepy. (3) She turned of the light and walked to bed. (4) She then brushed his teeth. (5) Lisa entered the bathroom. (6) She get into bed. (7) She went to sleep.

36. What change should you make to sentence 2?
a. change ***Her*** to ***She***
b. change ***getting*** to ***get***
c. change ***sleepy*** to ***sleepness***
d. make no change

37. What change should you make to sentence 3?
a. change ***She*** to ***Her***
b. change ***of*** to ***off***
c. change ***walked*** to ***walking***
d. make no change

38. What change should you make to sentence 4?
a. change ***She*** to ***Her***
b. change ***brushed*** to ***brush***
c. change ***his*** to ***her***
d. make no change

39. For a better sequence of events, sentence 3 should move _____.
a. after sentence 1
b. before sentence 3
c. before sentnece 5
d. before sentence 6

40. For a better sequence of events sentence 4 should move _____.
a. before sentence 3
b. after sentence 6
c. before sentence 1
d. before sentence 2

Name ______________________ Date ______________

TEST • Unit 1 *(continued)*

I. ➤ **Writing** *(20 points)*

> **Writing Prompt** Write an informational text about your favorite subject in school. Describe the subject and tell why it is your favorite. Use the Planning Guide to help you write.

Planning Guide

- ❏ Ask yourself these questions:
  - **a.** What is my favorite subject in school?
  - **b.** Why is it my favorite subject in school?
  - **c.** What facts do I know about it that can help me describe it?
- ❏ Use your answers to these questions in your writing.
- ❏ Make sure that your writing is clearly organized.

Name ______________________________ Date ______________ Grade

QUIZ Unit 2 • Chapter 1

A. ➤ Vocabulary: Choose the correct answer. *(20 points: 4 points each)*

1. Learning to use _____ words will help you to write well.
a. long
b. short
c. precise
d. funny

2. Eating vegetables is good for you. A more exact word for good is _____.
a. fine
b. kind
c. strong
d. healthy

3. Pedro's room is very clean. A more exact word for clean is _____.
a. large
b. spotless
c. messy
d. crowded

vid•e•o /ˈvɪdɪoʊ/ *n.* television or videotape pictures [Latin *videre* to see]

4. What is the meaning of the Latin root of video in the definition above?
a. to like
b. to hear
c. to see
d. to go

sub•tract /səbˈtraekt/ *v.* to take away from another [Latin *subtractus* to draw from under]

5. What is the meaning of the Latin root of subtract in the definition above?
a. to draw a picture
b. to draw from under
c. to buy something
d. to find out the cost

B. ➤ Text Structure/Elements of Literature: Read and choose the correct answer. *(36 points: 4 points each)*

"Family Reunion"

1 Mirna had heard many stories about her family members. Some had interesting jobs. Others had interesting hobbies. Her grandmother had told her that most of her family used to live in one neighborhood, but they moved away for different reasons. Mirna was worried about meeting her relatives. Would they like each other? She glanced at the "Ramirez Family Reunion" sign at the park. Then she saw a group of smiling people. She knew that she had nothing to fear.

6. "Family Reunion" is an example of a _____.
a. drama
b. realistic fiction
c. poem
d. nonfiction text

7. This story could happen in real life because _____.
a. the setting is in an unusual place
b. the characters act differently than most people
c. the events could take place in a person's life
d. the main character does not act like most teens

8. Plot is the _____ in a story.
a. main character
b. events
c. climax
d. ending

9. Before Mirna goes to the reunion, she _____.
a. worries about meeting her relatives
b. talks to her parents
c. asks a friend to come
d. writes a letter to her grandmother

Name ______________________________ Date ____________________

QUIZ Unit 2 • Chapter 1 *(continued)*

10. Mirna's grandmother is important in the story's plot because she _____.
- **a.** plans the reunion
- **b.** makes the sign
- **c.** telephones the relatives
- **d.** tells the family's history

11. What event in the reading kept Mirna from knowing many of her family members?
- **a.** Some family members moved away from the neighborhood.
- **b.** Mirna's grandmother kept her away from them.
- **c.** Mirna moved far away from most of her family members.
- **d.** Some family members had hobbies that kept them away from home.

12. The most important part of the story is when _____.
- **a.** Mirna hears stories about her relatives
- **b.** Mirna takes up a new hobby
- **c.** Mirna's family goes on a vacation
- **d.** Mirna sees her relatives for the first time

13. Which event shows that Mirna's problem has been solved?
- **a.** She hears stories about her family's jobs.
- **b.** She knows that her relatives have interesting lives.
- **c.** She sees a sign that says "Ramirez Family Reunion."
- **d.** She sees her family members smiling at the park.

14. In the past, most of the Ramirez family _____.
- **a.** disliked each other
- **b.** lived in the same neighborhood
- **c.** visited the park
- **d.** wrote stories

C. ➤ Reading Strategies: Choose the correct answer. *(12 points: 4 points each)*

15. Clues a writer uses to tell a story are _____.
- **a.** problems
- **b.** text evidence
- **c.** solutions
- **d.** main ideas

16. Josh turned off the alarm clock, shut the curtain, and got back into bed. You can infer that _____.
- **a.** Josh wants to get up now
- **b.** Josh wants more sleep
- **c.** Josh will wake up his family
- **d.** Josh has trouble sleeping

17. Jen got a library book about a coin she found. You can infer that _____.
- **a.** Jen doesn't care about the coin
- **b.** Jen is interested in the coin
- **c.** Jen likes gold
- **d.** Jen collects money

D. ➤ Grammar/Usage: Choose the correct answer. *(12 points: 4 points each)*

18. The present progressive tense shows _____.
- **a.** an action that has been completed
- **b.** an action that is going on now
- **c.** words that are made up in a sentence
- **d.** words that help the noun

19. Manny _____ a new book.
- **a.** is reading
- **b.** are reading
- **c.** had reading
- **d.** were reading

20. Tanya _____ her relatives last week.
- **a.** visit
- **b.** is visiting
- **c.** was visit
- **d.** was visiting

E. ➤ Writing *(20 points)*

Writing Prompt Write a realistic fiction story. Use text evidence to tell what happens in your story.

Name ______________________ Date ______________ Grade

QUIZ Unit 2 • Chapter 2

A. ➤ Vocabulary: Choose the correct answer. *(28 points: 4 points each)*

1. To find information for a school report, use _____.
   a. reference sources
   b. made-up facts
   c. a book of folktales
   d. a friend's opinion

2. To find a word origin, look in a(n) _____.
   a. encyclopedia
   b. dictionary
   c. almanac
   d. atlas

3. Words that mean almost the same thing are called _____.
   a. opposites
   b. homonyms
   c. synonyms
   d. antonyms

4. _____ can be used to look at reference sources on a computer.
   a. A helper
   b. Material
   c. Software
   d. A printer

5. Adverbs tell about _____.
   a. people
   b. actions
   c. things
   d. places

6. Many adverbs end in the suffix _____.
   a. *-tion*
   b. *-ed*
   c. *-ness*
   d. *-ly*

7. The young sailor carefully steered the boat. Which word in the sentence is an adverb?
   a. new
   b. sailor
   c. carefully
   d. steered

B. Text Structure/Elements of Literature: Read and choose the correct answer. *(20 points: 4 points each)*

"Teamwork"

1 Lupe and Anna were excited. They were going on a rowboat with Anna's cousin, Kate. Kate rowed out onto the lake. Kate showed the girls how to row. They were having a lot of fun until Anna noticed that the boat was filling with water. Kate said, "Don't worry. We have life jackets. Get out and hold on to the boat. We'll get back to shore." They worked as a team and held onto the boat. They stayed calm. Kate was right—they made it back to shore safely.

8. "Teamwork" is a(n) _____.
   a. poem
   b. news story
   c. story of a person's life
   d. adventure story

9. The most exciting part of the story is when the girls _____.
   a. meet Kate
   b. first row out onto the lake
   c. see water in the boat
   d. stay calm

10. What is the girls' problem in the story?
    a. They do not have life jackets.
    b. They cannot swim.
    c. They are afraid their boat will sink.
    d. They do not know how to row.

11. How do the girls solve their problem?
    a. They call for help.
    b. They work as a team to get to shore.
    c. They fix the hole in the boat.
    d. They jump overboard and swim away.

Name ______________________ Date ______________

QUIZ Unit 2 • Chapter 2 *(continued)*

12. The girls handled a dangerous situation by _____.
- **a.** arguing with each other
- **b.** staying calm
- **c.** going their own ways
- **d.** getting their parents

C. Reading Strategies: Choose the correct answer. *(16 points: 4 points each)*

13. Lightning flashed in the black sky. The mood of this sentence is _____.
- **a.** frightening
- **b.** disappointed
- **c.** calm
- **d.** sad

14. Alex smiled when he looked at his trophy. The tone of this sentence is _____.
- **a.** happy
- **b.** angry
- **c.** busy
- **d.** nervous

15. Mrs. Kim helps her students after school even when she is tired. She is a great teacher. The tone of the sentence is _____.
- **a.** admiring
- **b.** serious
- **c.** dangerous
- **d.** unhappy

16. Marie lost the money that she had earned from her babysitting job. The mood of the sentence is _____.
- **a.** respectful
- **b.** glad
- **c.** sad
- **d.** scary

D. Grammar/Usage: Choose the correct answer. *(16 points: 4 points each)*

17. Use the word _____ when talking about the future.
- **a.** is
- **b.** were
- **c.** are
- **d.** will

18. Next week, the students _____ their trip to the museum.
- **a.** will enjoy
- **b.** has enjoyed
- **c.** am enjoyed
- **d.** is enjoying

19. Our team _____ play on that field next season.
- **a.** did not
- **b.** will not
- **c.** has not
- **d.** do not

20. My friend Juan will go to Lincoln School in the fall. Which group of words shows that the action will take place in the future?
- **a.** My friend Juan
- **b.** will go
- **c.** to Lincoln School
- **d.** in the fall

E. ➤ Writing *(20 points)*

Writing Prompt Write an adventure story that tells about an exciting event. Create characters who must solve a problem.

Name ______________________ Date ______________

Grade

QUIZ Unit 2 • Chapter 3

A. ➤ Vocabulary: Choose the correct answer. *(28 points: 4 points each)*

1. Context clues are _____.
- **a.** words that surround an unknown word
- **b.** words that are similar to a new word
- **c.** words that give minor details
- **d.** words that are new to a reader

2. Authors use glosses, or definitions, to _____.
- **a.** help readers understand new words
- **b.** make a list of the words used in a chapter
- **c.** tell readers which details are important
- **d.** let readers know when to use a dictionary

3. To call readers' attention to new words in a chapter, writers often _____.
- **a.** use pictures in a chapter
- **b.** give the meanings of the words at the end of the book
- **c.** tell the way the new words are pronounced
- **d.** place the words in boldface type

4. Pedro liked to learn new things, so he became a researcher in a hospital lab. Researcher means _____.
- **a.** someone who finds out information
- **b.** someone who is a patient in a hospital
- **c.** someone who enjoys going to school
- **d.** someone who tells the news

5. An Egyptian pharaoh had a lot of power over his kingdom. A pharaoh is _____.
- **a.** someone from a faraway country
- **b.** someone who ruled Egypt
- **c.** someone who is very intelligent
- **d.** someone who studied kings

6. If a store clerk undercharged Ray, then Ray paid _____.
- **a.** the correct price
- **b.** less than the correct price
- **c.** more than the correct price
- **d.** nothing

7. Mavis overpaid for a coat at the store. This means that Mavis _____.
- **a.** paid a fair price
- **b.** paid too much money
- **c.** bought something on sale
- **d.** got money in return

B. ➤ Text Structure/Elements of Literature: Read and choose the correct answer. *(16 points: 4 points each)*

"A Real Advantage"

1 Many students study a second language. At first, it may be hard to learn another language, however, most students get better with practice. Knowing a second language is one of the best skills that anyone can have. The business world offers many jobs for people who know a second language. They can work in banks, schools, and government offices. When people travel, they can use their language skills to talk to others.

8. "A Real Advantage" is a(n) _____.
- **a.** fictional story
- **b.** adventure story
- **c.** informational text
- **d.** play

9. The reading explains _____.
- **a.** what young people study in school
- **b.** why it is helpful to know a second language
- **c.** which jobs young people can get
- **d.** when students should start learning another language

Name ______________________________ Date ____________________

QUIZ Unit 2 • Chapter 3 *(continued)*

10. Learning a second language is difficult, but it gives people many advantages. The underlined word signals ____.
  a. a contrasting idea
  b. support for the same idea
  c. the writer wants to prove a point
  d. the writer wants to give a similar fact

11. At first, it may be hard to learn another language, however, most students get better with practice. Which word contrasts ideas?
  a. At
  b. first
  c. however
  d. most

C. Reading Strategies: Choose the correct answer. *(16 points: 4 points each)*

12. Which is an opinion?
  a. French is the language spoken in France.
  b. French is easy to learn.
  c. Mr. Jones teaches French.
  d. Lucy is a student in my French class.

13. Which is a fact?
  a. People in Canada speak French and English.
  b. English is more difficult than French.
  c. Canada is a beautiful country.
  d. Canada has better places to visit than the United States.

14. A fact is different from an opinion because ____.
  a. it tells about feelings
  b. it tells about a person's views
  c. it can be proven to be true or false
  d. it can be different for every person.

15. Facts should be used in an informational text because they ____.
  a. explain the writer's topic
  b. support the writer's feelings
  c. show if the writer's ideas are good
  d. connect the writer's ideas

D. Grammar/Usage: Choose the correct answer. *(20 points: 4 points each)*

16. Use a ____ verb to talk about things that are usually true or happen every day.
  a. present tense
  b. present progressive tense
  c. past tense
  d. past progressive tense

17. The cat ____ outside to find mice.
  a. go
  b. goes
  c. going
  d. is go

18. Many people ____ traveling to new places.
  a. enjoy
  b. enjoys
  c. enjoying
  d. is having

19. Dan ____ his cousin in Mexico every summer.
  a. am visit
  b. visits
  c. visiting
  d. are visiting

20. Today, most doctors ____ people to walk every day.
  a. advise
  b. advising
  c. was advisor
  d. is advised

E. ➤ Writing *(20 points)*

Writing Prompt Write an informational text. Include facts that explain your topic. Use transition words to connect your ideas.

Name ______________________________ Date ______________ Grade [ ]

QUIZ Unit 2 • Chapter 4

A. ➤ Vocabulary: Choose the correct answer. *(20 points: 4 points each)*

1. The dictionary shows how to say a word by using ____.
   a. symbols
   b. numbers
   c. pictures
   d. brackets

2. When a letter is silent, you do not ____ it.
   a. write
   b. spell
   c. read
   d. pronounce

> **knit** /nit/ *v.* to make clothes by connecting loops of yarn with long sticks: *She can knit her own socks.*

3. In the dictionary entry above, which letter in knit is silent?
   a. k
   b. n
   c. i
   d. t

4. Only two people stayed on the island. The underlined word means ____.
   a. also
   b. more than enough
   c. a number
   d. a word used before a verb

5. On a nice day, I like ____ eat lunch outside.
   a. to
   b. two
   c. too
   d. toe

B. ➤ Text Structure/Elements of Literature: Read and choose the correct answer. *(28 points: 4 points each)*

> "The Hike"
>
> 1 Eddie and Gina liked to take pictures for the school newspaper. When their class planned a hike in the park, they offered to take pictures. As the others walked ahead, they stopped to take a few pictures. Suddenly, it was very quiet. They realized they were alone. Gina shouted, "We're lost! What will we do?" Eddie took out a map and a flashlight. "Here, let's take this path," Eddie said confidently. "We'll find our way." Soon they heard their friends' voices.

6. "The Hike" is a(n) ____.
   a. fiction story that could be true
   b. play that reads like a poem
   c. first-person narrative
   d. informational text

7. The story takes place ____.
   a. on a made up island
   b. in a park
   c. in a classroom
   d. in a dream

8. "The Hike" could be based on a true story because people can ____.
   a. get lost
   b. ask animals for help
   c. communicate with nature
   d. make daylight last longer

9. The theme of "The Hike" is similar to the theme of "Island of the Blue Dolphins" because both stories tell how people ____.
   a. can survive by using their skills
   b. get frightened when they are lost
   c. give up when they face challenges
   d. need to rely on others for help

Name ______________________________ Date ____________________

QUIZ Unit 2 • Chapter 4 (continued)

10. In both stories, the main characters solve their problems by ____.
    a. being strong and confident
    b. asking neighbors for advice
    c. finding food to eat
    d. keeping wild animals away

11. Karana and Eddie both use their ____ to find a way out of a difficult situation.
    a. friends
    b. thinking skills
    c. writing skills
    d. books

12. When faced with a problem, Gina is different from Eddie because she ____.
    a. remains calm
    b. cries out for help
    c. reacts with fear
    d. makes a plan

C. ➤ Reading Strategies: Choose the correct answer. *(16 points: 4 points each)*

13. When you paraphrase, you ____.
    a. give your opinion about what you read
    b. tell part of a text in your own words
    c. create a new ending for a story
    d. provide more details for a story

14. Paraphrasing helps you to ____.
    a. guess what you will read
    b. decide if you like a story
    c. recall what you have read
    d. learn about the author

15. Paul yawned and stretched out on the chair after baseball practice. Choose the best paraphrase for this sentence.
    a. Paul liked to play baseball.
    b. Paul was tired after baseball practice.
    c. Paul had just gotten up.
    d. Paul wanted to try out for the baseball team.

16. Ms. Gonzales makes tortillas to welcome new neighbors. Choose the paraphrase for this sentence.
    a. Ms. Gonzales only cooks when new neighbors move in.
    b. Ms. Gonzales likes to welcome newcomers with treats.
    c. Ms. Gonzales likes bread.
    d. Ms. Gonzales's neighbors are hungry.

D. ➤ Grammar/Usage: Choose the correct answer. *(16 points: 4 points each)*

17. Tense tells ____.
    a. what kind of action occurred
    b. when an action happened
    c. why an action took place
    d. who did an action

18. Fabio cut the grass. This sentence is in the ____ tense.
    a. future c. present
    b. past d. present perfect

19. The past perfect tense tells about an action that ____.
    a. happened before another action
    b. happens at the same time
    c. was caused by another action
    d. will happen in the future

20. I had sketched the picture before I painted it. Which words show the past perfect tense?
    a. had sketched c. before I
    b. the picture d. painted it

E. ➤ Writing *(20 points)*

Writing Prompt Write a realistic fiction story. Create characters, a plot, and a setting that could be real.

Name ______________________________ Date ______________ Grade

QUIZ Unit 2 • Chapter 5

A. ➤ Vocabulary: Choose the correct answer. *(20 points: 4 points each)*

1. On a word wheel, write words that are ____.
   - **a.** different
   - **b.** interesting
   - **c.** easy
   - **d.** related

2. Which word belongs on a word wheel with the words recycle, save, and conserve?
   - **a.** protect
   - **b.** pick
   - **c.** careless
   - **d.** waste

3. Adding the letters *-ion* to a word makes it a(n) ____.
   - **a.** verb
   - **b.** adjective
   - **c.** adverb
   - **d.** noun

4. The animals risk extinction. What is the root word of extinction?
   - **a.** ex
   - **b.** tinction
   - **c.** extinct
   - **d.** ion

5. The telephone is a ____ when you are studying.
   - **a.** distract
   - **b.** distracted
   - **c.** distractness
   - **d.** distraction

B. ➤ Text Structure/Elements of Literature: Read and choose the correct answer. *(20 points: 4 points each)*

> "Reuse It or Lose It!"
>
> 1 When you save glass, plastic, and paper, you are recycling. Recycling means using materials again to save natural resources. Once materials are collected, they are sent to places called recycling plants. At these plants, the materials are prepared to be reused, or used again. Recycling something as simple as the daily newspaper can save many trees. It will make sure that our natural resources will not be used up so quickly.

6. "Reuse It or Lose It!" is a(n) ____.
   - **a.** adventure fiction
   - **b.** informational text
   - **c.** poem
   - **d.** fable

7. "Reuse It or Lose It!" ____.
   - **a.** gives a description
   - **b.** compares two things
   - **c.** explains a topic
   - **d.** offers an argument

8. Writers often write informational texts about ____.
   - **a.** famous people
   - **b.** science topics
   - **c.** mythical persons
   - **d.** folktale animals

9. In this text, the writer organizes facts ____.
   - **a.** in a deductive way
   - **b.** in an inductive way
   - **c.** according to time order
   - **d.** from least to most important

Name ______________________ Date ______________________

QUIZ Unit 2 • Chapter 5 *(continued)*

10. In a deductive paragraph, which of the following comes first?
a. a question
b. the most important point
c. facts about the topic
d. minor details

C. ➤ Reading Strategies: Choose the correct answer. *(20 points: 4 points each)*

11. A(n) _____ is the reason why something happens.
a. example
b. cause
c. effect
d. opinion

12. A(n) _____ happens because of a cause.
a. fact
b. effect
c. reason
d. description

13. The dog is barking loudly. What will be a likely effect?
a. The neighbors will wake up.
b. The dog will go to sleep.
c. The alarm clock will ring.
d. The sun will rise.

14. Melda is very tired. What is a likely cause of Melda's tiredness?
a. She rested all day.
b. She worked hard.
c. She feels tired.
d. She will go to sleep.

15. The weather is cold. What is the likely effect of the weather?
a. People will dress warmly.
b. People will go to the beaches.
c. It will be a hot day.
d. The wind will stop blowing.

D. ➤ Grammar/Usage: Choose the correct answer. *(20 points: 4 points each)*

16. A dependent clause is used with a(n) _____.
a. subject
b. verb
c. phrase
d. independent clause

17. Students report that they recycle paper and plastic at their school. The independent clause is _____.
a. students report
b. that they recycle
c. paper and plastic
d. at their school

18. Many dependent clauses begin with _____.
a. *that*
b. *and*
c. *or*
d. *but*

19. We researched the idea that eating breakfast gives you energy. What is the dependent clause?
a. We researched
b. We researched the idea
c. the idea that eating breakfast
d. that eating breakfast gives you energy

20. You will see that the library can be an exciting place. What is the independent clause?
a. you will see
b. you will see that
c. that the library
d. can be an exciting place

E. ➤ Writing *(20 points)*

Writing Prompt Write an informational text about a subject you know a lot about. Use inductive or deductive organization.

Name ______________________ Date ______________ Grade

TEST • Unit 2

A. ➤ Reading

The Forest Fire

My Notes

1 The forest fire had been burning for two weeks on the western slope of the mountain. Now it was moving east—in their direction. Jason's mother was leaving to check on an elderly neighbor, but as she hurried toward the car she repeated their plan for the hundredth time. If the fire came over the hill, he was to get Sara into the sailboat and sail to the middle of the lake.

2 Jason watched the car start down the forest road; he quickly lost sight of it in the dense, acrid smoke. Smoke filled the spaces between tree trunks like the fog did in summer. Jason's eyes were stinging.

3 His mother had been gone only a few minutes when Jason heard a *whoosh.* He looked up and saw the top of the hill explode in flames. He dashed into the house to find his sister. Sara was sitting on the floor, hugging her stuffed panda. He didn't have time to pry it out of her grasp, so he raced toward the boat half carrying, half dragging his sister and the huge panda.

4 From the middle of the lake, they watched the fire leap from treetop to treetop. "Our house is going to burn," Sara whimpered and buried her face in the panda's chest.

5 "Maybe not. Look." Jason pointed. The treetops nearest the house were ablaze, but the fire had jumped right over the roof. Now, a firefighting plane began to circle overhead. Jason wrapped his arms around Sara.

Name ______________________ Date ______________

TEST • Unit 2 *(continued)*

B. ➤ Reading Comprehension: Choose the correct answer. *(20 points: 2 points each)*

1. In "The Forest Fire," why is it important that the author tells that the fire was moving east?
- **a.** to show that another fire is burning in the far distance
- **b.** to foreshadow that it will move closer to Jason's home
- **c.** to show that Sara spotted the fire first
- **d.** to predict who will put out the fire

2. How long had the forest fire been burning?
- **a.** one week
- **b.** two weeks
- **c.** a day
- **d.** a month

3. Why did Jason's mother have to leave?
- **a.** to help a neighbor
- **b.** to take care of Sara
- **c.** to go shopping
- **d.** to check on the fire

4. What did Jason and his mother plan to do with Sara?
- **a.** take her to a safe place
- **b.** buy her a new bear
- **c.** take her for a car ride
- **d.** allow her to visit a friend

5. It was hard for Jason to see his mother drive away in her car because of the ____.
- **a.** wind
- **b.** clouds
- **c.** smoke
- **d.** rain

6. Jason would know it was time to leave when ____.
- **a.** He saw the fire at the top of the hill.
- **b.** He heard many cars leaving.
- **c.** He got a call from his neighbor.
- **d.** He saw firefighters arrive.

7. Sara hugged her toy bear because she was ____.
- **a.** happy
- **b.** lonely
- **c.** scared
- **d.** hungry

8. Jason did not take the bear out of Sara's hands because ____.
- **a.** they had to leave very quickly.
- **b.** they wanted to give it to their mother.
- **c.** he liked the bear too.
- **d.** he did not want Sara to cry.

9. What happened to the roof of the house?
- **a.** The fire spread to it from the trees.
- **b.** The fire jumped over it.
- **c.** The fire burned part of it.
- **d.** The fire made it collapse.

10. Jason and his sister knew everything would be alright when they saw ____.
- **a.** birds
- **b.** a helicopter
- **c.** rain clouds
- **d.** firefighting planes

TEST • Unit 2 *(continued)*

C. ➤ Reading Strategies: Choose the correct answer. *(10 points: 2 points each)*

11. From the story, you can infer that Jason's mother is a _____ person.
- **a.** selfish
- **b.** quiet
- **c.** kind
- **d.** happy

12. The mood of the story is _____.
- **a.** exciting
- **b.** calm
- **c.** mysterious
- **d.** joyful

13. Which is an opinion?
- **a.** In a forest fire, a lake is the safest place to be.
- **b.** Fire can quickly spread from tree to tree.
- **c.** Jason's mother drove a car away from her home.
- **d.** Jason tried to help his younger sister, Sara.

14. What is the best way to paraphrase paragraph 3?
- **a.** Jason missed his mother very much after she left.
- **b.** Sara's favorite toy was her stuffed bear.
- **c.** Jason heard an unusual noise in the house that scared his sister.
- **d.** Jason ran to the sailboat with his sister and the panda to escape the fire.

15. The picture of the boat is important to the story because Jason and Sara use it to _____.
- **a.** go fishing
- **b.** escape the fire
- **c.** look for their mother
- **d.** help their neighbors

D. ➤ Elements of Literature: Read and choose the correct answer. (*10 points: 2 points each)*

16. Which event made Jason take action?
- **a.** He knew his neighbor was in trouble.
- **b.** He heard his sister crying.
- **c.** He saw the fire spreading.
- **d.** He heard a warning siren.

17. How did Jason and Sara solve their problem?
- **a.** They went on a short vacation.
- **b.** They asked a friend for advice.
- **c.** They hid in their house.
- **d.** They got far away from the fire.

18. Jason's mother was leaving to check on an elderly neighbor, but as she hurried toward the car she repeated their plan for the hundredth time. Which is the transition word?
- **a.** check
- **b.** but
- **c.** she
- **d.** plan

19. How are the themes of "The Forest Fire" and "Island of the Blue Dolphins" similar?
- **a.** Both stories tell a funny story for all to enjoy.
- **b.** Both stories encourage readers to go on an adventure.
- **c.** Both stories deal with overcoming a problem.
- **d.** Both stories describe the perfect place to go on vacation.

Name ________________________ Date ________________

TEST • *Unit 2* *(continued)*

Jamie and Sara watched the fire leap from treetop to treetop.
Sara cried in the panda's chest.
The fire jumped over the roof of Jamie's house.
A firefighting plane began to circle overhead.

20. Look at the chart. What is the organization of the details in the chart?
a. inductive
b. deductive
c. order of importance
d. chronological order

E. ➤ Vocabulary: Choose the correct answer. *(10 points: 2 points each)*

21. Sara was sitting on the floor, hugging her enormous stuffed bear. A more precise word for hugging is ____.
a. patting
b. spinning
c. clutching
d. tapping

22. To find more information about forest fires, you can look in a(n) ____.
a. poetry book
b. adventure story
c. reference source
d. book of plays

23. The treetops nearest the house were ablaze, but the fire had jumped right over the roof. Ablaze means ____.
a. very tall
b. bright
c. beautiful
d. on fire

24. He dashed into the house to find his sister. The underlined word ____.
a. is a number
b. means more than enough
c. is a word used before a verb
d. means also

25. Which word belongs on a word wheel with the words hurried, dashed, and raced?
a. walked
b. sat
c. ran
d. marched

Name ______________________ Date ______________

TEST • Unit 2 (continued)

F. ➤ Grammar/Usage: Choose the correct answer. *(10 points: 2 points each)*

26. People were running from the fire. The underlined verb phrase is in the ____ tense.
- **a.** present
- **b.** present progressive
- **c.** past
- **d.** past progressive

27. Tomorrow a reporter ____ the family about the fire.
- **a.** interviewed
- **b.** interviewing
- **c.** will interview
- **d.** had interviewed

28. Firefighters battle fires every day. The tense of the underlined verb is ____.
- **a.** present
- **b.** past
- **c.** future
- **d.** past perfect

29. I had written my sister a letter before I visited her. The tense of this sentence is ____.
- **a.** present
- **b.** past
- **c.** future
- **d.** past perfect

30. It is important that we succeed. Which group of words is a dependent clause?
- **a.** It is important
- **b.** It is important that
- **c.** that we succeed
- **d.** we succeed

G. ➤ Writing Conventions *(10 points: 2 points each)*

31. On tuesday, I will meet a friend at the school library. Which word should begin with a capital letter?
- **a.** tuesday
- **b.** friend
- **c.** school
- **d.** library

32. Which sentence should end with an exclamation point?
- **a.** Please pass the salt
- **b.** Stop that bus
- **c.** Our team will play next Friday night
- **d.** Which movie did you see

33. Which sentence is correct?
- **a.** It is nice to meet you, I said.
- **b.** Martin said, "I like to read mysteries."
- **c.** Anna answered, I finished the report today.
- **d.** Our class will discuss the story, replied Ms. Mills.

34. Mary's family traveled all over the U.S last year. Which change should be made to the sentence?
- **a.** Place a comma after Mary.
- **b.** Make the first letter in family a capital letter.
- **c.** Add a period after S in U.S.
- **d.** Change the period to a question mark.

35. In science, we studied animals plants, and flowers. A comma should be added after the word ____.
- **a.** In
- **b.** studied
- **c.** animals
- **d.** and

Name ______________________________ Date ____________________

TEST • Unit 2 *(continued)*

H. ➤ Editing *(10 points: 2 points each)*

Be Prepared

(1) It is important to be prepared for emergencies. (2) One day, I babysit for my little brother, Tommy. (3) There was a sudden storm. (4) The power went off and it got very dark. (5) I quick went to get the flashlight from under my bed. (6) Tommy followed me. (7) He was careful, so he tripped. (8) He scraped his knee. (9) I got him a bandage, and then we sit down on the floor in my room. (10) I used the flashlight to read him a story. (11) We had fun. (12) Now I would teach Tommy to be prepared, too!

36. What change should you make to sentence 2?
- **a.** change ***One*** to ***Some***
- **b.** change ***babysit*** to ***was babysitting***
- **c.** change ***my*** to ***mine***
- **d.** make no change

37. What change should you make to sentence 5?
- **a.** change ***quick*** to ***quickly***
- **b.** change ***quick*** to ***quicked***
- **c.** change ***to get*** to ***was getting***
- **d.** make no change

38. What change should you make to sentence 7?
- **a.** change ***He*** to ***She***
- **b.** change ***so*** to ***but***
- **c.** change ***tripped*** to ***trip***
- **d.** make no change

39. What change should you make to sentence 9?
- **a.** change ***him*** to ***he***
- **b.** change ***we*** to ***us***
- **c.** change ***sit*** to ***sat***
- **d.** make no change

40. What change should you make to sentence 12?
- **a.** change ***Now*** to ***Then***
- **b.** change ***would*** to ***will***
- **c.** change ***too*** to ***to***
- **d.** make no change

I. ➤ Writing *(20 points)*

Writing Prompt Write a realistic adventure story. Create characters that act like real people. Show how the characters solve a problem. Use the Planning Guide to help you write.

Planning Guide
- ❏ Tell what will happen in the story.
- ❏ Tell what excitement or danger your characters will face.
- ❏ Write a beginning, a middle, and an end.
- ❏ Use precise words to explain how your characters act and feel.

Name ______________________ Date ______________ Grade

QUIZ Unit 3 • Chapter 1

A. ➤ Vocabulary: Choose the correct answer. *(20 points: 4 points each)*

1. Multiple meaning words are ____.
- **a.** words that are spelled differently
- **b.** words that mean more than one thing
- **c.** word parts added to the beginning of words
- **d.** words that have only one meaning

2. I ate a roll for breakfast. In this sentence, the word roll means ____.
- **a.** to turn over
- **b.** to make flat
- **c.** a type of bread
- **d.** a list of names

3. The suffix *-ity* means ____.
- **a.** before
- **b.** without
- **c.** the condition or state of
- **d.** the beginning and end of something

4. ____ means "the condition or state of being equal."
- **a.** Equaled
- **b.** Equation
- **c.** Equality
- **d.** Equally

5. The older students show more ____ than the younger ones.
- **a.** mature
- **b.** immature
- **c.** maturity
- **d.** maturer

B. ➤ Text Structure/Elements of Literature: Read and choose the correct answer. *(24 points: 4 points each)*

"Snowfall"

1 The snow falls
gently to the ground.

2 The snow leaves behind
quiet and peace.

6. The words in this poem do not rhyme. This type of poem is called ____.
- **a.** free verse
- **b.** slant rhyme
- **c.** imagery
- **d.** apostrophe

7. Which group of words from the poem is an example of repetition?
- **a.** The snow
- **b.** the ground
- **c.** leaves behind
- **d.** quiet and peace

8. ____ is the author's attitude toward what he or she is writing about.
- **a.** Mood
- **b.** Style
- **c.** Figurative language
- **d.** Tone

9. Which of these words describes the mood of this poem?
- **a.** angry
- **b.** scared
- **c.** silly
- **d.** peaceful

10. Description in a poem creates a(n) ____ in your mind.
- **a.** image
- **b.** synonym
- **c.** rhyme
- **d.** graphic aid

Name ______________________________ Date ______________________

QUIZ Unit 3 • Chapter 1 *(continued)*

11. What image is described in the poem?
- **a.** a white blanket
- **b.** falling snow
- **c.** the ground
- **d.** leaves

C. ➤ Reading Strategies: Choose the correct answer. *(16 points: 4 points each)*

12. _____ is language that means something different than what it says.
- **a.** Inference
- **b.** Capitalization
- **c.** Figurative language
- **d.** Foreign language

13. A metaphor _____.
- **a.** says that two things are different
- **b.** says that one thing is another
- **c.** tells what an object does
- **d.** tells about a special place

14. Which of these sentences has an example of a metaphor?
- **a.** The dog ate his food.
- **b.** I like playing sports.
- **c.** That child is a tornado.
- **d.** Carmen rides her bicycle fast.

15. The colorful kite is a beautiful, soaring bird. The kite is like _____.
- **a.** a color
- **b.** another kite
- **c.** the sky
- **d.** a bird

D. ➤ Grammar/Usage: Choose the correct answer. *(20 points: 4 points each)*

16. An _____ can make a noun possessive.
- **a.** adjective
- **b.** antonym
- **c.** apostrophe
- **d.** adverb

17. Which of these words is a plural possessive noun?
- **a.** doctors
- **b.** doctors'
- **c.** doctor's
- **d.** doctor

18. The _____ jacket was torn.
- **a.** boy
- **b.** boys
- **c.** boy's
- **d.** boys'

19. The three _____ dog is friendly.
- **a.** sister
- **b.** sister's
- **c.** sisters
- **d.** sisters'

20. _____ father works at a bank.
- **a.** Michael
- **b.** Michael's
- **c.** Michaels
- **d.** Michaels'

E. ➤ Writing *(20 points)*

Writing Prompt Write a poem about a journey that you would like to take. Use figurative language.

Name ______________________ Date ______________

Grade

QUIZ Unit 3 • Chapter 2

A. ➤ Vocabulary: Choose the correct answer. *(28 points: 4 points each)*

1. Anxiously means _____.
a. in a bored way
b. in a quiet way
c. in a worried way
d. in a tired way

2. Juan was _____ because his mother gave him a fun game.
a. delighted
b. difficult
c. depressed
d. damaged

3. Lila loved her cat very much. When it was lost, Lila cried _____.
a. happily
b. mournfully
c. joyfully
d. impatiently

4. I jumped because I was _____ to hear the loud noise.
a. waiting
b. guilty
c. ready
d. shocked

5. It is uncommon for students to like all of their subjects equally. Uncommon means _____.
a. very common
b. not common
c. sometimes common
d. town common

6. Unsealed means _____.
a. sealed
b. almost sealed
c. not sealed
d. ready to be sealed

7. Which word means "not fair"?
a. fairly
b. fairer
c. fairness
d. unfair

B. Text Structure/Elements of Literature: Read and choose the correct answer. *(20 points: 4 points each)*

"Across the Ocean"

1 It was the year of 1624. Jill knew that she had to act brave. But inside she was terrified to leave her home.

2 "Mother, I'm scared to leave England," said Jill. "What if Plymouth Colony is a terrible place?"

3 Jill's mother smiled at her daughter. "It's natural to feel afraid. But you'll like Plymouth Colony. Besides, your best friend, Julia, is there."

8. "Across the Ocean" is a(n) _____.
a. historical fiction
b. poem
c. legend
d. informational text

9. The setting of "Across the Ocean" is _____.
a. not told in the story
b. guessed by the reader
c. a made-up place and time
d. a real place and time

10. _____ is the feeling that the reader gets from the text.
a. Dialogue
b. Setting
c. Mood
d. Simile

11. What is the mood of "Across the Ocean"?
a. worried
b. calm
c. lonely
d. excited

Name ______________________________ Date ______________________

QUIZ Unit 3 • Chapter 2 *(continued)*

12. Alberto cheered when he won the game. What is the mood of this sentence?
    - **a.** angry
    - **b.** sad
    - **c.** happy
    - **d.** peaceful

C. ➤ Reading Strategies: Choose the correct answer. *(12 points: 4 points each)*

13. To paraphrase is to ____.
    - **a.** guess what will happen next in a story
    - **b.** use your own words to tell part of a text
    - **c.** list details that support the main idea of a text
    - **d.** decide whether a statement is fact or opinion

14. Ming says, "I hope you to move to Bay Town, Joe." What is the best paraphrase of the sentence?
    - **a.** Ming tells Joe not to come to Bay Town.
    - **b.** Joe says that he is waiting for Ming in Bay Town.
    - **c.** Ming says that he hopes Joe will move to Bay Town.
    - **d.** Joe says that he is scared to move to Bay Town.

15. "Sir," asked Mario, "do you know how to get to city hall?" What is the best paraphrase of the sentence?
    - **a.** Mario asked a man for directions to city hall.
    - **b.** A man gave Mario directions to the city.
    - **c.** Mario needed to meet a friend at city hall.
    - **d.** Mario asked Sir to go to the city.

D. ➤ Grammar/Usage: Choose the correct answer. *(20 points: 4 points each)*

16. A ____ is a word that is used in the place of a noun.
    - **a.** verb
    - **b.** proper noun
    - **c.** conjunction
    - **d.** pronoun

17. Which of these words is an object pronoun?
    - **a.** I
    - **b.** he
    - **c.** they
    - **d.** them

18. He wrote on it. In this sentence, the subject pronoun is ____.
    - **a.** He
    - **b.** it
    - **c.** wrote
    - **d.** on

19. She will make it. In this sentence, the object pronoun is ____.
    - **a.** She
    - **b.** it
    - **c.** make
    - **d.** will

20. We like the baker. He gives ____ free cookies.
    - **a.** we
    - **b.** you
    - **c.** they
    - **d.** us

E. ➤ Writing *(20 points)*

> **Writing Prompt** Write a historical fiction story. Use a real time and place from history in your story.

Name ______________________ Date ______________ Grade

QUIZ Unit 3 • Chapter 3

A. ➤ Vocabulary: Choose the correct answer. *(28 points: 4 points each)*

1. Our experiment was a failure. The volcano did not erupt. In this sentence, failure means _____.
   a. not a success
   b. a success
   c. a difficult task
   d. a happy event

2. The vase shattered into pieces. In this sentence, shattered means _____.
   a. grew
   b. built
   c. broke
   d. ran

3. The racecar whizzed around the corner. In this sentence, whizzed means _____.
   a. slept
   b. sped
   c. danced
   d. wrote

4. A prefix is a _____.
   a. group of letters added to the beginning of a word
   b. group of letters added to the middle of a word
   c. new word added to the end of another word
   d. new word made up of two smaller words

5. The prefix *bi-* means _____.
   a. zero
   b. one
   c. two
   d. three

6. A person who is able to speak two languages is _____.
   a. unilingual
   b. lingually
   c. bilingual
   d. lingualer

7. A tradition that is shared by two cultures is called _____.
   a. biannual
   b. bicultural
   c. noncultural
   d. cultured

B. ➤ Text Structure/Elements of Literature: Read and choose the correct answer. *(20 points: 4 points each)*

"The Space Pilot"

1 Today was Nobu's first day as a space pilot! Space pilots flew spaceships all over the galaxy. They flew people to Saturn for vacation. They flew people to the Moon for a visit. Nobu liked traveling more than anything. Space pilots traveled a lot!

2 Nobu rushed outside. He was ready to start his day. But then he saw the sky. It was full of dark clouds. Nobu shivered as a strange feeling came over him.

8. "The Space Pilot" is _____.
   a. a poem
   b. science fiction
   c. historical nonfiction
   d. a play

9. Science fiction is usually set in _____.
   a. a school
   b. a spaceship
   c. the past
   d. the future

10. Science fiction uses ideas from _____ to tell a story.
    a. social studies
    b. music
    c. science
    d. art

Name ______________________ Date ______________

QUIZ Unit 3 • Chapter 3 *(continued)*

11. When _____, authors give clues about what will happen later in a story.
    a. foreshadowing
    b. summarizing
    c. setting
    d. directing

12. In "The Space Pilot," what foreshadows that something bad might happen?
    a. Nobu woke up.
    b. Nobu was excited to start work.
    c. Nobu raced out the door.
    d. Nobu shivered when he saw the dark clouds.

C. ➤ Reading Strategies: Choose the correct answer. *(12 points: 4 points each)*

13. To predict is to _____.
    a. decide whether something is true or false
    b. use text clues to guess what will happen next
    c. notice how two things are different
    d. use pictures to understand a text

14. Eddy is hungry and goes into the kitchen. You can predict that Eddy will _____.
    a. watch TV
    b. do his homework
    c. find something to eat
    d. take his dog for a walk

15. Nico is very tired. You can predict that Nico will _____.
    a. go to bed
    b. play football
    c. drink water
    d. run in a race

D. ➤ Grammar/Usage: Choose the correct answer. *(20 points: 4 points each)*

16. All contractions have _____.
    a. exclamation points
    b. question marks
    c. periods
    d. apostrophes

17. We've is made up of which two words?
    a. we and will
    b. we and have
    c. we and would
    d. we and are

18. What is the contraction of did + not?
    a. did've
    b. did'll
    c. didn't
    d. did's

19. What is the contraction of she + is?
    a. she'll
    b. she's
    c. she'd
    d. she're

20. I'd have come sooner if I knew you were waiting for me. I'd is made up of _____.
    a. I and do
    b. I and had
    c. I and would
    d. I and will

E. ➤ Writing *(20 points)*

Writing Prompt Write a paragraph that describes a place in the future. Describe what the place looks like, what people can do there, and what year it is.

Name ______________________________ Date ______________ Grade

QUIZ Unit 3 • Chapter 4

A. ➤ Vocabulary: Choose the correct answer. *(28 points: 4 points each)*

1. What is the root word of unhappy?
- **a.** un
- **b.** not
- **c.** happy
- **d.** happ

2. The prefix *re-* means "again." The word redo means to ____.
- **a.** do something again
- **b.** do something before
- **c.** do something after
- **d.** do something first

3. The suffixes *-er* and *-est* ____.
- **a.** compare things
- **b.** describe actions
- **c.** join two sentences
- **d.** mean "not"

4. Which of these is a superlative adjective?
- **a.** brightest
- **b.** brightly
- **c.** bright
- **d.** brighter

5. What is the root word of loudest?
- **a.** est
- **b.** loud
- **c.** loudly
- **d.** louder

6. Grandfather is the oldest person in our family. Oldest means ____.
- **a.** no one is younger
- **b.** no one is older
- **c.** everyone is older
- **d.** all are the same age

7. Wassim is the tallest boy in class. Tallest means ____.
- **a.** Wassim is taller than most boys in class.
- **b.** All the boys in class are taller than Wassim.
- **c.** Wassim is taller than all the boys in class.
- **d.** Most of the boys in class are taller than Wassim.

B. ➤ Text Structure/Elements of Literature: Read and choose the correct answer. *(20 points: 4 points each)*

"The Secret Life of Chocolate"

1 Where does chocolate come from? Chocolate comes from cacao beans. Cacao beans grow on special trees. First, the cacao beans are picked and dried in the sun. Then they are roasted. Their outer shells are removed. Next, the beans are crushed to make a sticky paste. The chocolate paste is mixed with other ingredients. The mixture is heated. Finally, the chocolate is ready!

8. "The Secret Life of Chocolate" is a(n) ____.
- **a.** autobiography
- **b.** myth
- **c.** informational text
- **d.** historical narrative

9. What is the topic of "The Secret Life of Chocolate"?
- **a.** the different types of chocolate
- **b.** how to grow your own cacao tree
- **c.** when chocolate was discovered
- **d.** how chocolate is made

10. One fact stated in "The Secret Life of Chocolate" is that ____.
- **a.** chocolate is bitter
- **b.** chocolate liquor is dried
- **c.** cacao beans grow on cacao trees
- **d.** cacao beans are handmade

Name ______________________________ Date ______________________

QUIZ Unit 3 • Chapter 4 *(continued)*

11. In ____, an author makes a general statement and then gives details about that statement.
a. deductive presentation
b. figurative language
c. comparing
d. contrasting

12. "The Secret Life of Chocolate" begins with a ____.
a. comparison
b. question
c. metaphor
d. definition

C. ➤ Reading Strategies: Choose the correct answer. *(12 points: 4 points each)*

13. When you reread, you ____.
a. draw pictures in your mind
b. put events in the order they occurred
c. carefully read a text again
d. use text clues to make a guess

14. Before you read an informational text, you should ____.
a. record important facts
b. reread the text
c. paraphrase the text and author's thoughts
d. ask questions about the title and topic

15. What can you do if you do not understand a sentence the first time you read it?
a. reread the sentence aloud
b. predict what will happen next
c. underline the pronoun in the sentence
d. write a paragraph about the sentence

D. ➤ Grammar/Usage: Choose the correct answer. *(20 points: 4 points each)*

16. Many adjectives use the word ____ to become superlative.
a. more
b. some
c. most
d. all

17. Which of these shows happy as a superlative adjective?
a. happiest
b. happyest
c. happily
d. happier

18. My garden is the ____ place in the world!
a. wonderful
b. wonderfulest
c. most wonderfulest
d. most wonderful

19. That is the ____ cat I have ever seen.
a. most big
b. biggest
c. bigger
d. most biggest

20. Gary was the ____ person at the party.
a. nicest
b. nicer
c. most nice
d. more nicest

E. ➤ Writing *(20 points)*

> **Writing Prompt** Write an informational text about space. Use facts about space that you learned in the chapter to help you write.

Name ______________________________ Date ________________ Grade

QUIZ Unit 3 • Chapter 5

A. ➤ Vocabulary: Choose the correct answer. *(20 points: 4 points each)*

1. To understand the meaning of a word in a text, _____.
- **a.** use the context and your experiences
- **b.** guess what will happen next
- **c.** summarize what you read
- **d.** draw conclusions about what you read

2. To help remember the meanings of words, you can _____.
- **a.** find the main idea of the text
- **b.** make a word list
- **c.** circle the adjectives in a sentence
- **d.** make inferences

3. Aya was late so she bolted down the hall. In this sentence, bolted means _____.
- **a.** laughed loudly
- **b.** watched quietly
- **c.** ran quickly
- **d.** painted over

4. Joseph abbreviated his name to Joe. In this sentence, abbreviated means _____.
- **a.** opened
- **b.** sold
- **c.** shortened
- **d.** lengthened

5. People traveled West in covered wagons. Covered wagons could be found in a list of words about _____.
- **a.** music
- **b.** science
- **c.** art
- **d.** social studies

B. ➤ Text Structure/Elements of Literature: Read and choose the correct answer. *(32 points: 4 points each)*

"The Scat Singer"

1 Ella Fitzgerald was born in 1917 in Virginia. Her singing career began at the age of 16. Chick Webb, a musician, discovered her singing talents at the Apollo Theater. Fitzgerald's career soon soared.

2 Ella Fitzgerald sang in concerts all over the world. She was considered one of the world's greatest scat singers. She used nonsense words to make different sounds with her voice. Today, many singers copy Fitzgerald's style of scat singing.

6. "The Scat Singer" is _____.
- **a.** nonfiction
- **b.** science fiction
- **c.** a play
- **d.** a myth

7. In nonfiction, events are _____.
- **a.** made-up
- **b.** real
- **c.** both real and made-up
- **d.** based on real events

8. Which event led to Ella Fitzgerald becoming a famous singer?
- **a.** Ella Fitzgerld singing at age 16 for people in Virginia
- **b.** Ella Fitzgerald going to concert halls to help strengthen her singing
- **c.** Chick Webb discovering Ella Fitzgerald's talented singing
- **d.** Chick Webb teaching Ella Fitzgerald how to sing scat

Name ______________________________ Date ______________________

QUIZ Unit 3 • Chapter 5 *(continued)*

"The Greatest Night"

1 It was a warm, New York night in 1934. A young girl approached the center stage at the Apollo Theater. The young girl was there to dance. But she didn't. Chick could sense her shyness. Someone said in a loud whisper, "Do something!" The young Ella Fitzgerald opened her mouth and began singing. Ella's voice was beautiful! The bandleader, Chick Webb, played music as Ella continued to sing. Chick thought, "She has the most amazing voice that I have ever heard!"

9. "The Greatest Night" is a(n) _____.
a. historical fiction
b. informational text
c. autobiography
d. mystery

10. _____ are what a character is like.
a. Styles **c.** Motivations
b. Traits **d.** Images

11. As a young girl, Ella was_____.
a. angry **c.** bold
b. brave **d.** shy

12. Chick was motivated to play muic by _____.
a. someone's whispering
b. the crowd's cheering
c. Ella's singing
d. Ella's dancing

13. How are historical fiction and nonfiction alike?
a. both are made-up
b. both are set in a real time and place
c. both are set in a made-up time and place
d. both use made-up characters

C. ➤ Reading Strategies: Choose the correct answer. *(16 points: 4 points each)*

14. _____ shows how things are different.
a. Comparing **c.** Inferring
b. Predicting **d.** Contrasting

15. His house and her house are both yellow. This sentence _____ the two houses.
a. compares **c.** contrasts
b. summarizes **d.** interviews

16. David's hair is short. Manuel's hair is long. These sentences contrast _____.
a. height **c.** hair color
b. hair length **d.** names

17. Which compares bears and rabbits?
a. Bears are big, and rabbits are small.
b. Bears eat meat, and rabbits eat vegetables.
c. Bears and rabbits are types of animals.
d. Bears run, and rabbits hop.

D. ➤ Grammar/Usage: Choose the correct answer. *(12 points: 4 points each)*

18. Adverbs describe _____.
a. nouns and pronouns
b. verbs and adjectives
c. nouns and prepositions
d. conjunctions only

19. He walks and talks slowly. The adverb in this sentence is _____.
a. he **c.** talks
b. and **d.** slowly

20. Many adverbs have the suffix _____.
a. *-ion* **c.** *-er*
b. *-y* **d.** *-ly*

E. ➤ Writing *(20 points)*

Writing Prompt Write a historical fiction story. Use real events and people from the past in your story.

Name ______________________ Date ______________ Grade

TEST • Unit 3

A. ➤ Reading

The Great Space Race

My Notes

1 In the 1950s, two large nations began a contest against one another. This bicultural contest was called the "Space Race." It was between the United States and the Soviet Union. Both nations wanted to learn more about space. They also wanted to achieve the greatest successes in space exploration.

2 The Soviet Union launched *Sputnik* in October 1957. *Sputnik* was the first satellite sent into space. In October 1959, the Soviet Union sent the first spacecraft around the moon. It sent the first spacecraft to circle around Earth in April 1961. The first person to walk in space was also from the Soviet Union.

3 What effect did these Soviet successes have on the United States? One effect was that some people became uninterested in the United States' part in the Space Race. It seemed like the nation was losing the race, even though it worked hard to keep up with the Soviet Union.

4 In May 1961, President John F. Kennedy spoke to Americans about his dream for exploring space. He said, "I believe that this nation should commit itself to the goal before this decade is out, of landing a man on the moon and returning him safely to the Earth." Some people thought the president's dream was unrealistic. But the president didn't. He believed that his dream for the United States would happen.

5 On July 20, 1969, people watched TV with great excitement. They watched a spacecraft of victory land on a strange gray surface. A man in a white space suit climbed out. This man was an American named Neil Armstrong. He was the first human to land on the moon!

6 When the United States landed on the moon, many people felt that it had won the Space Race. Yet, both the Americans and the Soviets had learned much about space travel. Today, countries around the world use this knowledge. They work together to continue to explore space.

Name ______________________________ Date ____________________

TEST • Unit 3 *(continued)*

B. ➤ Reading Comprehension: Choose the correct answer. *(20 points: 2 points each)*

1. The Space Race was ____.
   a. a bicycle race
   b. a race to explore space
   c. a presidential election
   d. over by 1950

2. Which of these things helped show that the Soviet Union was winning the Space Race?
   a. people watching TV
   b. the United States landing on the moon
   c. the launch of *Sputnik*
   d. countries working together to explore space

3. Which event happened *before* the first spacecraft circled Earth?
   a. The first spacecraft circled the moon.
   b. President Kennedy told Americans his dream.
   c. The United States landed on the moon.
   d. The Space Race ended.

4. What is the main idea of paragraph 6?
   a. At first, the United States was losing the Space Race.
   b. Some Americans did not like President Kennedy.
   c. The Space Race was an exciting time in history.
   d. People learned a lot about space because of the Space Race.

5. Why did people think Kennedy's dream was unrealistic?
   a. The United States had already sent a person to the moon.
   b. It was too easy to send a person to the moon.
   c. The United States needed more time to send a person to the moon.
   d. The United States should send a person to one of the planets instead.

6. Why was Neil Armstrong important?
   a. He helped the Soviet Union win the Space Race.
   b. He was the first person to walk on the moon.
   c. He was the first person to circle Earth.
   d. He was president of the United States.

7. Paragraphs 2, 3, and 4 are important because they show that ____.
   a. the United States was losing the Space Race at first
   b. many Americans had TV sets
   c. the United States had learned a lot about space exploration
   d. many Americans were angry about the Space Race

8. Which word describes President Kennedy's attitude in paragraph 4?
   a. worried
   b. determined
   c. afraid
   d. calm

9. Based on paragraph 3, some Americans lost interest in the Space Race because they ____.
   a. did not like President Kennedy
   b. thought the Space Race cost too much money
   c. thought the United States would lose the race
   d. believed people did not belong in space

10. What is the purpose of the picture in the reading?
    a. to explain how President Kennedy felt
    b. to help show how a spaceship looks
    c. to help describe a scientist
    d. to entertain readers with pretty art

Name ______________________________ Date ____________________

TEST • Unit 3 (continued)

C. ➤ Reading Strategies: Choose the correct answer. *(10 points: 2 points each)*

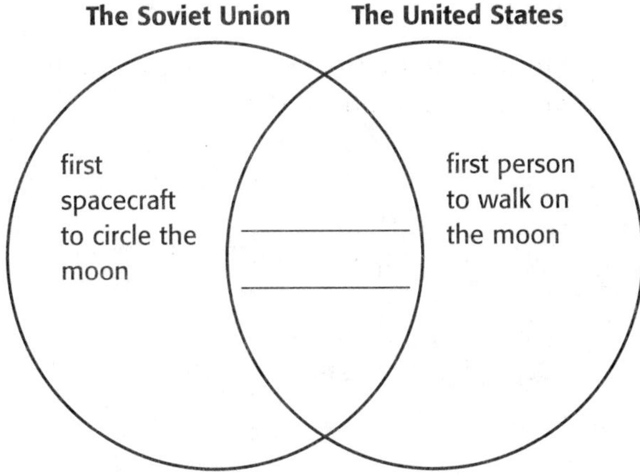

11. Use the Venn diagram to compare the United States and the Soviet Union. Both the Soviet Union and the United States ____.

a. sent people to another planet
b. wanted to win the Space Race
c. sent the first person to walk in space
d. did not want to send a person to the moon

12. Which sentence paraphrases President Kennedy's statement in paragraph 4?

a. I think the Soviet Union will send a person to the moon next year.
b. It is impossible to send a person to the moon in the next ten years.
c. The United States should work to send a person to the moon and bring him back before 1970.
d. The United States and the Soviet Union should work together to send a person to the moon and back.

13. From paragraph 6, you can predict that ____.

a. people will continue to learn about space
b. there will be another Space Race
c. only the United States will keep exploring space
d. people will discover a new planet

14. Which question is answered in paragraph 3?

a. Who was Neil Armstrong?
b. In what year did the Space Race begin?
c. Which countries were involved in the Space Race?
d. How did Soviet advances affect the United States?

15. In paragraph 5, what does the author mean by the phrase <u>spacecraft of victory</u>?

a. The spacecraft was amazing.
b. The spacecraft flew faster than other spacecrafts.
c. The spacecraft was larger than the Soviet spacecrafts.
d. The spacecraft helped the United States win the Space Race.

D. ➤ Elements of Literature: Choose the correct answer. *(10 points: 2 points each)*

16. "The Great Space Race" is ____.

a. a poem
b. an informational text
c. historical fiction
d. science fiction

17. President Kennedy said the United States would send a person to the moon before the end of the decade. What could be his reason for saying this?

a. to pull the United States out of the Space Race
b. to help the Soviet Union win the Space Race
c. to get Americans interested in winning the Space Race
d. to stop Americans from caring about space travel

18. What is the mood of paragraph 5?

a. angry
b. excited
c. sad
d. bored

TEST • Unit 3 *(continued)*

19. Which sentence from the text tells you that the United States will probably land on the moon first?
- **a.** He believed that his dream for the United States would happen.
- **b.** This contest was called the "Space Race."
- **c.** Today, countries around the world use this knowledge.
- **d.** *Sputnik* was the first satellite sent into space.

20. In paragraph ____, the author shows how the United States and the Soviet Union were similar.
- **a.** 6
- **b.** 4
- **c.** 3
- **d.** 1

E. ➤ **Vocabulary:** Choose the correct answer. *(10 points: 2 points each)*

21. From the context of paragraph 4, you know that the word unrealistic probably means ____.
- **a.** likely to happen
- **b.** popular
- **c.** not likely to happen
- **d.** interesting

22. In paragraph 1, the word bicultural means ____.
- **a.** of three cultures
- **b.** of one culture
- **c.** of four cultures
- **d.** of two cultures

> **land** /lænd/ *n.* **1** soil, earth **2** an area owned as property **3** a nation, country *v.* **4** to reach a particular place

23. Read this dictionary entry for the word land. Which definition most closely matches the meaning of land in paragraph 5?
- **a.** 1
- **b.** 2
- **c.** 3
- **d.** 4

24. In paragraph 3, the word uninterested tells you that the people were ____.
- **a.** interesting
- **b.** not interested
- **c.** smart
- **d.** not ready

25. In paragraph 1, the word greatest tells you that both the United States and the Soviet Union wanted to____.
- **a.** explore more parts of space than all other countries
- **b.** learn just a little bit about space
- **c.** help each other explore space
- **d.** have fun while exploring space

F. ➤ **Grammar/Usage:** Choose the correct answer. *(10 points: 2 points each)*

26. Which is a superlative adjective?
- **a.** flattest
- **b.** flatter
- **c.** big
- **d.** bigger

27. Which sentence is correct?
- **a.** My mothers car is green.
- **b.** My mothers' car is green.
- **c.** My mother's car is green.
- **d.** My mother car is green.

28. The contraction I'm contains the words I and ____.
- **a.** would
- **b.** am
- **c.** will
- **d.** is

Name ______________________ Date ______________

TEST • Unit 3 *(continued)*

29. You are happy today, Joe! The subject pronoun in this sentence is ____.
a. are
b. happy
c. You
d. today

30. She walked slowly through the door. The adverb in this sentence is ____.
a. She
b. ran
c. through
d. slowly

G. ➤ Writing Conventions: Choose the correct answer. *(10 points: 2 points each)*

31. Which shows the correct spelling of 55?
a. fifty five
b. fifty five-
c. fifty-five
d. -fifty five

32. You go to school to get an ____. Which spelling correctly completes the sentence?
a. iducateshun
b. edjukashen
c. educashingon
d. education

23. I live in Fresno California. To make this sentence correct, place a(n) ____ between Fresno and California.
a. comma
b. period
c. apostrophe
d. question mark

24. Which sentence shows correct capitalization?
a. The blue dress was made in china.
b. Kelly speaks spanish.
c. The country of Japan is in Asia.
d. Hugo visited mexico once.

25. Morning comes after ____.
a. nite
b. night
c. knight
d. nit

Name ______________________________ Date ______________________

TEST • Unit 3 *(continued)*

H. ➤ Editing: Read and choose the correct answer. *(10 points: 2 points each)*

(1) Yesterday, Kevin and I saw the school play, "Wind in the Trees." (2) It was the wonderfulest play we had ever seen! (3) The play was about a boy and his fight to save a 100-year-old oak tree in Oakwood Texas. (4) Our friend Sophie played the part of the ancient oak tree. (5) Kevin is a member of the Spanish club. (6) Her costume was beautiful! (7) I cant wait to see the next school play.

36. What change should you make to sentence 1?
- **a.** Change ***Kevin*** to ***kevin***
- **b.** delete the quotation marks around ***"Wind in the Trees"***
- **c.** ***"Wind in the Trees"*** should be in bold-faced type
- **d.** make no change

37. What change should you make to sentence 2?
- **a.** change ***It*** to ***They***
- **b.** change ***wonderfulest*** to ***most wonderful***
- **c.** change ***ever*** to ***never***
- **d.** make no change

38. What change should you make to sentence 3?
- **a.** change ***play*** to ***Play***
- **b.** change ***100-year-old*** to ***100 year old***
- **c.** add a comma between ***Oakwood*** and ***Texas***
- **d.** make no change

39. For a more logical order, sentence 5 should _____.
- **a.** be taken out of the paragraph
- **b.** move to the beginning of the paragraph
- **c.** move to the end of the paragraph
- **d.** stay where it is

40. What change should you make to sentence 7?
- **a.** change ***cant*** to ***can't***
- **b.** change to ***see*** to ***seeing***
- **c.** change ***school play*** to ***School Play***
- **d.** make no change

I. ➤ Writing *(20 points)*

Writing Prompt Write an informational text about your neighborhood to share with visitors. Include facts about three interesting places to visit. Use the Planning Guide to help you write.

Planning Guide
- ❑ Brainstorm three interesting places in your neighborhood.
- ❑ Under the name of each place, write facts about the place.
- ❑ Use your facts to write your informational text.
- ❑ Use a voice in your writing that is appropriate for your audience.

VISIONS TEST Unit 3

Name ______________________ Date ______________ Grade

MID-BOOK EXAM

A. ➤ Reading

The Golden Flute

1 Long ago, in a village in India, defenseless villagers lived in constant fear of tiger attacks. A young boy named Bansi lived in the village.

2 Wandering through the forest one day, Bansi noticed a glistening object near a tree. "What is that?" he wondered. Then, Bansi realized it was a golden flute.

3 Bansi put the instrument to his lips and began to play. To his surprise, the flute produced a soothing melody that caused the trees to sway and the animals to sleep. "This is amazing!" thought Bansi.

4 As darkness fell, Bansi heard piercing screams from the village. Realizing tigers were attacking the village, Bansi scurried home. He raised the flute to his lips and blew. The tigers' ferocious, snarling roars turned into yawns. Then the tigers slowly strolled away.

5 Bansi was a hero. To this day, people in India still talk about Bansi and the power of his golden flute.

My Notes

B. ➤ Reading Comprehension: Choose the correct answer. *(20 points: 2 points each)*

1. In "The Golden Flute," where does Bansi live?
- **a.** in a large city in India
- **b.** in a small village in India
- **c.** in a medium town on Mars
- **d.** in an old forest

2. In "The Golden Flute," Bansi calls the flute amazing because it is _____.
- **a.** mysterious
- **b.** unpleasant
- **c.** free
- **d.** simple

3. In "The Golden Flute," the villagers thought Bansi was a hero because he _____.
- **a.** could play the flute very well
- **b.** saved the village from the tigers
- **c.** sold the flute and gave the money to the village
- **d.** liked to walk through the forest

Name ______________________________ Date ______________________

MID-BOOK EXAM *(continued)*

Life on Mars

1 Three months had passed since Gracie moved from Earth to New Austin, the largest city on Mars. Gracie's father had answered an ad and found a job there. He brought Gracie and her mother with him to Mars.

> **WANTED IMMEDIATELY:**
>
> Experienced Botanist to help grow plants in completely enclosed environment.
>
> Must be willing to relocate to Mars.

2 In many ways, Gracie's life on Mars was similar to her life on Earth. She attended school and went to movies. She even made new friends.

3 Despite these similarities, Gracie still longed for life on Earth. She missed strolling through the forest, and inhaling fresh mountain air. On Mars, she had to stay indoors because she couldn't breathe the air. If she did go outside, Gracie had to wear a special suit supplied with oxygen.

4 Gracie often daydreamed about her old life, about feeling a spring wind gently rushing through an open window. At night she dreamed of waking to a sparrow's melodious chirp. When she wakes, however, the only sound is the endless rumble of oxygen being pumped through the vents.

My Notes

4. Look at the want ad pictured in "Life on Mars." From the ad, you can conclude that Gracie's father is a ____.
- **a.** history teacher
- **b.** basketball coach
- **c.** scientist who studies plants
- **d.** reporter for a newspaper

5. In "Life on Mars," what caused Gracie to move to Mars?
- **a.** Her mother liked the weather there.
- **b.** Gracie's parents disliked living on Earth.
- **c.** Gracie wanted to go to college there.
- **d.** Gracie's father found a job in New Austin.

6. Complete the Venn Diagram. In "Life on Mars," how are Earth and Mars similar?
- **a.** Gracie has friends.
- **b.** People use a special suit to breathe.
- **c.** People spent a lot of time outdoors.
- **d.** Gracie opens the windows.

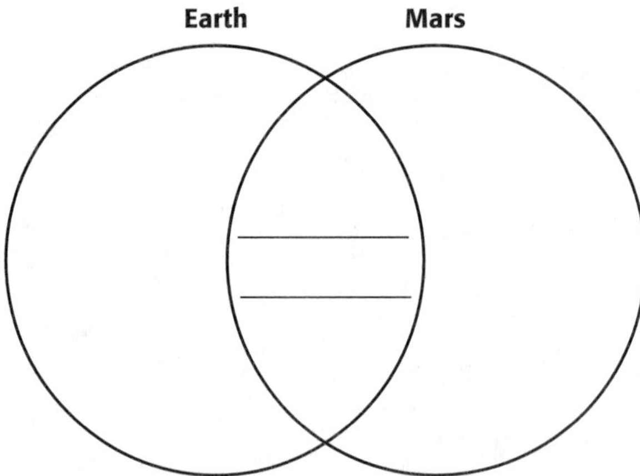

7. The author tells "Life on Mars" from Gracie's point of view. This helps the reader understand ____.
- **a.** the equipment people use to breathe on Mars
- **b.** Gracie's mother's thoughts about living on Earth
- **c.** the special activities that people can do on Mars
- **d.** Gracie's feelings about her new life on Mars

Name ______________________ Date ______________

MID-BOOK EXAM (continued)

8. Which sentence correctly compares the two readings?
- **a.** "Life on Mars" happens in the future, and "The Golden Flute" happens in the past.
- **b.** "Life on Mars" happens in a city, and "The Golden Flute" happens in a village.
- **c.** Both readings happen in a time other than the present.
- **d.** Both readings happen in a big city.

9. In "Life on Mars," the fact that Gracie dreams of birds and forests tells the reader that Gracie ____.
- **a.** is an excellent student
- **b.** loves the outdoors
- **c.** is a scientist
- **d.** will grow her own vegetables on Mars

10. In "Life on Mars," what happened three months ago?
- **a.** Gracie's family moved to Mars.
- **b.** Gracie began school in New Austin.
- **c.** Gracie had her first daydream about Earth.
- **d.** Gracie's family moved from Mars to Earth.

C. ➤ Reading Strategies: Choose the correct answer. *(10 points: 2 points each)*

11. Which statement correctly contrasts "The Golden Flute" and "Life on Mars"?
- **a.** "The Golden Flute" is a legend, and "Life on Mars" is science fiction.
- **b.** Both "The Golden Flute" and "Life on Mars" are legends.
- **c.** "The Golden Flute" is a poem, and "Life on Mars" is historical nonfiction.
- **d.** Both "The Golden Flute" and "Life on Mars" are science fiction.

12. In "Life on Mars," which detail tells you that Gracie misses Earth?
- **a.** Gracie goes to the movies on Mars.
- **b.** Gracie's father found a job in New Austin.
- **c.** Gracie daydreams about opening the window.
- **d.** Gracie's new friends are a lot of fun.

13. What can you predict will happen in the village because of Bansi's golden flute?
- **a.** The villagers are no longer afraid of tiger attacks.
- **b.** The villagers destroy Bansi's golden flute.
- **c.** Bansi finds a better flute.
- **d.** Bansi learns to play other musical instruments.

14. The tigers' fierce, snarling roars turned into yawns. Which is the best paraphrase of this sentence?
- **a.** The tigers growled and showed their large sharp teeth.
- **b.** The tigers stopped growling and started to yawn.
- **c.** The tigers became very angry.
- **d.** The tigers' teeth became sleepy.

15. In "Life on Mars," what is the author's attitude toward Gracie?
- **a.** The author dislikes Gracie.
- **b.** The author is jealous of Gracie.
- **c.** The author feels sorry for Gracie.
- **d.** The author is angry at Gracie.

Name ______________________________ Date ______________

MID-BOOK EXAM *(continued)*

D. ➤ Elements of Literature: Choose the correct answer. *(10 points: 2 points each)*

16. In "Life on Mars," the setting is important because it ____.
- **a.** causes Gracie to move to New Austin
- **b.** describes Gracie's father's new job
- **c.** tells the meaning of important words
- **d.** helps the reader understand Gracie's new life

17. Then, Bansi realized it was a golden flute. Which correctly rewrites this sentence as a quote?
- **a.** It's a golden flute, said Bansi.
- **b.** "It's a golden flute," said Bansi.
- **c.** "It's a golden flute, said Bansi"
- **d.** "It's a golden flute said Bansi"

18. The problem in "The Golden Flute" is ____.
- **a.** Bansi cannot play the flute
- **b.** the villagers argue with one another
- **c.** tigers often attack the village
- **d.** Bansi cannot find his golden flute

19. Reread paragraph 4 in both "The Golden Flute" and "Life on Mars." Which statement contrasts the moods of these paragraphs?
- **a.** "The Golden Flute" is exciting and "Life on Mars" is sad.
- **b.** "The Golden Flute" is sad and "Life on Mars" is happy.
- **c.** "The Golden Flute" is happy and "Life on Mars" is funny.
- **d.** "The Golden Flute" is angry and "Life on Mars" is scary.

20. Despite these similarities, Gracie still longed for life on Earth. In this sentence, the transition word is ____.
- **a.** similarities
- **b.** longed
- **c.** these
- **d.** despite

E. ➤ Vocabulary: Choose the correct answer. *(10 points: 2 points each)*

21. Which word from "Life on Mars" means had a dream during the day?
- **a.** daydreamed
- **b.** rumble
- **c.** outdoors
- **d.** attended

22. The word melody comes from the Greek word melōidía, meaning "singing." From this information, you know that melodious means ____.
- **a.** in a faraway place
- **b.** a feeling of great sadness
- **c.** pleasantly musical
- **d.** a person from long ago

23. In paragraph 1 of "The Golden Flute," the word defenseless tells you that the villagers were ____.
- **a.** interested in tigers
- **b.** without defenses
- **c.** without supplies
- **d.** very intelligent

24. In paragraph 4 of "Life on Mars," the word gently helps you understand that the wind is ____.
- **a.** rough and harsh
- **b.** warm and wet
- **c.** strong and cold
- **d.** soft and mild

25. In "Life on Mars," the context of paragraph 3 tells you that inhaling means ____.
- **a.** smelling
- **b.** giving
- **c.** smiling at
- **d.** breathing in

Name ______________________ Date ______________

MID-BOOK EXAM (continued)

F. ➤ Grammar: Choose the correct answer. *(10 points: 2 points each)*

26. I want to go outside. I have to work. Which correctly combines these two sentences with the conjunction but?
    a. But I want to go outside, I have to work.
    b. I want to go outside. I have but to work.
    c. I want to go outside, but I have to work.
    d. I but have to work. I want to go outside.

27. Marisa cleaned the kitchen, and then she went shopping. In this sentence, the pronoun referent is ____.
    a. then
    b. Marisa
    c. cleaned
    d. she

28. The party had ended before I arrived. In this sentence, had ended is in the ____.
    a. past perfect tense
    b. present progressive tense
    c. past tense
    d. future tense

29. The family lives in a small, cozy apartment. The prepositional phrase in this sentence is ____.
    a. lives in a
    b. small, cozy apartment
    c. in a small, cozy apartment
    d. The family lives

30. Which sentence is correct?
    a. Rauls mother is a doctor's.
    b. Rauls mother's is a doctor.
    c. Raul mother is a doctor.
    d. Raul's mother is a doctor.

G. ➤ Writing Conventions: Choose the correct answer. *(10 points: 2 points each)*

31. Which shows the correct use of a comma?
    a. 1,5
    b. 350,0
    c. 2,000
    d. ,800

32. Which sentence is correct?
    a. On Monday, I go to art class.
    b. Miguel's favorite day of the week is saturday.
    c. Remember to vote on tuesday!
    d. Next wednesday is Grandmother's birthday.

33. What is the plural form of life?
    a. leefes
    b. lives
    c. live
    d. life

34. ____ said Stefan. Which correctly completes the sentence?
    a. "hello,"
    b. Hello
    c. hello
    d. "Hello,"

35. What is the plural form of capacity?
    a. caps
    b. capacitys
    c. capacities
    d. cities

Name ______________________ Date ______________________

MID-BOOK EXAM *(continued)*

H. ➤ Editing: Read and choose the correct answer. *(10 points: 2 points each)*

(1) The Amazon River is one of the world's greatest rivers. (2) At about 4,000 miles long, it is the second longer river on Earth! (3) It also carry more water than any other river on the planet. (4) Every minute, about 28 billion gallons of water had flowed from the Amazon River to the ocean! (5) The river contains so much water even though it is in an extremely rainy area. (6) Every year, the land around the Amazon receives about 400 inches of rain! (7) That is enough rain to ensure that the Amazon River was flowing for a long time.

36. What change should you make to sentence 2?
- **a.** change ***4,000*** to ***40,00***
- **b.** change ***longer*** to ***longest***
- **c.** change ***earth*** to ***Earth***
- **d.** make no change

37. What change should you make to sentence 3?
- **a.** change ***It*** to ***They***
- **b.** change ***carry*** to ***carries***
- **c.** change ***on*** to ***in***
- **d.** make no change

38. What change should you make to sentence 4?
- **a.** change ***Every*** to ***Any***
- **b.** change had ***flowed*** to ***flows***
- **c.** change ***Amazon River*** to ***amazon river***
- **d.** make no change

39. What change should you make to sentence 5?
- **a.** change ***so*** to ***too***
- **b.** change ***even though*** to ***but***
- **c.** change ***even though*** to ***because***
- **d.** make no change

40. What change should you make to sentence 7?
- **a.** change ***is*** to ***was***
- **b.** change ***Amazon River*** to ***amazon river***
- **c.** change ***was flowing*** to ***will be flowing***
- **d.** make no change

I. Writing *(20 points)*

Writing Prompt Write a five-paragraph story about a mysterious event. The event can be real or made-up. The characters in the story will solve the mystery. Use the Planning Guide to help you write.

Planning Guide

- ❑ Ask yourself the following questions:
  - **a.** What is the mysterious event?
  - **b.** When does the event happen?
  - **c.** Where does the event happen?
  - **d.** Who are the characters?
  - **e.** How do the characters solve the mystery?
- ❑ Use adverbs and adjectives to describe characters and events and to create a feeling of suspense.
- ❑ Include dialogue (what characters say to each other).
- ❑ Write a beginning, a middle, and an end.

Name ______________________________ Date ________________ Grade

QUIZ Unit 4 • Chapter 1

A. ➤ Vocabulary: Choose the correct answer. *(28 points: 4 points each)*

1. Vivid verbs make writing more ____.
   - **a.** ordinary
   - **b.** simple
   - **c.** exact
   - **d.** dull

2. The speeding car drove by. A vivid verb for drove is ____.
   - **a.** raced
   - **b.** crawled
   - **c.** sparkled
   - **d.** inspected

3. Maria shuts the door loudly. A vivid verb for shuts is ____.
   - **a.** leaps
   - **b.** slams
   - **c.** tears
   - **d.** howls

4. ____ meaning is the dictionary definition of a word.
   - **a.** Connotative
   - **b.** Reflective
   - **c.** Inductive
   - **d.** Denotative

5. ____ meaning is your feelings about a word.
   - **a.** Denotative
   - **b.** Figurative
   - **c.** Connotative
   - **d.** Instructive

6. The funny movie made me smile. The denotative meaning of smile is ____.
   - **a.** feel good
   - **b.** turn the lips up at the corners
   - **c.** feel sad
   - **d.** salty liquid from the eye

7. They fussed over who should go first in the game. The denotative meaning of fussed is ____.
   - **a.** agreed
   - **b.** played
   - **c.** rested
   - **d.** argued

B. ➤ Text Structure/Elements of Literature: Read and choose the correct answer. *(24 points: 4 points each)*

"My House"

1 My house:
Winks its windows at me in the glittering sunlight.
Hugs me with its strong, brick walls.

2 My house:
Talks to me as I walk up its creaky, wooden stairs.
Is a good friend.

8. A stanza is ____.
   - **a.** a group of lines in a poem
   - **b.** rhyming words in a poem
   - **c.** the third line of a poem
   - **d.** the title of a short story

9. The speaker of a poem is ____.
   - **a.** always the poet
   - **b.** always a person
   - **c.** the main character in the poem
   - **d.** the voice that is speaking in the poem

10. Which of these senses is used to describe the stairs in the poem?
    - **a.** touch
    - **b.** hearing
    - **c.** taste
    - **d.** smell

Name ______________________ Date ______________________

QUIZ Unit 4 • Chapter 1 *(continued)*

11. Personification is _____.
a. showing how two things are different
b. putting events in chronological order
c. giving an object human characteristics
d. writing to inform the reader

12. In the poem, the speaker compares the house to _____.
a. sunlight
b. a creaky stair
c. a brick wall
d. a friend

13. Which is an example of personification?
a. The water was cold.
b. The bell screamed.
c. Juan smiled brightly.
d. The man spoke loudly.

C. ➤ Reading Strategies: Choose the correct answer. *(12 points: 4 points each)*

14. _____ are pictures in your mind.
a. Stanzas
b. Sense words
c. Mental images
d. Facts

15. Which sentence helps a reader form the strongest mental image?
a. The dog barked.
b. Laurie wore a dress to Daniela's party.
c. Carlos laughed at the joke.
d. Huge, gray waves crashed into the sandy beach.

16. Which sentence helps a reader form the strongest mental image of Ivan?
a. Ivan is very nice.
b. Ivan is very thin with shiny, black hair.
c. Ivan is good at math and football.
d. Ivan is a student.

D. ➤ Grammar/Usage: Choose the correct answer. *(16 points: 4 points each)*

17. To change an adjective that ends with *y* into its comparative form, _____.
a. change the *y* to *i* and then add *-er*
b. drop the *y* and then add *-est*
c. add *-er*
d. add *-est*

18. The pool is _____ in the summer than in the winter.
a. busy
b. bus
c. busier
d. busiest

19. I sit _____ to the window than Jayna does.
a. close
b. closing
c. closest
d. closer

20. My dog is _____ than your dog.
a. friend
b. friendlier
c. friendlyer
d. friendliest

E. ➤ Writing *(20 points)*

Writing Prompt Write a poem that describes an everyday object. Use personification and vivid verbs.

Name ______________________ Date ______________ Grade

QUIZ Unit 4 • Chapter 2

A. ➤ Vocabulary: Choose the correct answer. *(28 points: 4 points each)*

1. You can use a(n) ____ to find a word's definition, pronunciation, part of speech, and derivation.
   a. encyclopedia
   b. dictionary
   c. thesaurus
   d. synonym finder

> **for•get** /fərˊgɛt/ *v.* **1** to not remember, drop from memory without intending to [from Old English *forgietan*]

2. In this dictionary entry, what part of speech is *forget?*
   a. adjective
   b. noun
   c. adverb
   d. verb

3. Derivation of a word tells its ____.
   a. history
   b. part of speech
   c. placement in sentences
   d. meaning in context

4. In the dictionary entry above, the definition of *forget* is ____.
   a. /fərˊget/
   b. to not remember
   c. the one who can remember
   d. Old English *forgietan*

5. The contraction aren't has the words ____.
   a. are and not
   b. is and not
   c. are and would
   d. will and not

6. Which of these forms the contraction of the words do and not?
   a. didn't
   b. can't
   c. isn't
   d. don't

7. Ben ____ going to school today.
   a. isn't
   b. didn't
   c. won't
   d. can't

B. ➤ Text Structure/Elements of Literature: Read and choose the correct answer. *(20 points: 4 points each)*

> "Sun and Moon"
>
> 1 Many years ago it was decided that Sun and Moon shall never meet. Neither Sun nor Moon knew that the other existed. One day, Sun caught sight of Moon. He moved across the sky to say hello. But Moon was frightened and ran away. Ever since, Sun has been chasing Moon across the sky, trying to say hello.

8. Myths are often ____.
   a. about people who do not have special powers
   b. told aloud from generation to generation
   c. true stories
   d. never told aloud

9. "Sun and Moon" is a myth because it ____.
   a. explains an event in nature
   b. tells the true story of a person's life
   c. teaches readers about events in history
   d. gives scientific information about how something works

10. "Sun and Moon" explains why ____.
    a. the stars twinkle all around the moon at night
    b. the sky looks blue during the day and at night
    c. the sun is bigger and brighter than the moon
    d. the sun and moon are not seen in the sky together

QUIZ Unit 4 • Chapter 2 *(continued)*

11. In foreshadowing, authors ____.
- **a.** try to make the reader laugh
- **b.** explain how to do something
- **c.** give clues about what will happen later in a story
- **d.** describe their opinions of characters in a story

12. Which words from the story foreshadow the ending of "Sun and Moon"?
- **a.** Sun caught sight of Moon
- **b.** moved across the sky to say hello
- **c.** it was decided that Sun and Moon should never meet
- **d.** Sun has been chasing Moon across the sky

C. ➤ Reading Strategies: Choose the correct answer. *(20 points: 4 points each)*

13. ____ is the order in which events happen.
- **a.** Present tense
- **b.** A synonym
- **c.** Chronology
- **d.** The main idea

14. A ____ can help you keep track of when events happen.
- **a.** bar graph
- **b.** timeline
- **c.** dictionary
- **d.** word wheel

15. Kim got into her car and drove away. She stopped to eat something. Then she went to work. What did Kim do right before she went to work?
- **a.** went for a run
- **b.** got into her car
- **c.** drove away
- **d.** stopped to eat something

16. Malcolm left school. He stopped by the library. He met his friend Tony there. What did Malcolm do right after he left school?
- **a.** went back to school
- **b.** stopped by the library
- **c.** met his friend Tony
- **d.** picked up a book

17. Consuela tied her shoes. She grabbed her coat. She then ran down the stairs and out the door. What did Consuela do right before she ran down the stairs?
- **a.** grabbed her coat
- **b.** tied her shoes
- **c.** ran around
- **d.** went out the door

D. ➤ Grammar/Usage: Choose the correct answer. *(12 points: 4 points each)*

18. Irregular past tense verbs ____.
- **a.** describe actions that will happen in the future
- **b.** sometimes use the ending *ed*
- **c.** do not use the ending *ed*
- **d.** describe actions that are happening right now

19. The past tense form of make is ____.
- **a.** made
- **b.** maked
- **c.** maded
- **d.** remake

20. Knew is the past tense of ____.
- **a.** new
- **b.** kneel
- **c.** need
- **d.** know

E. ➤ Writing *(20 points)*

Writing Prompt Write a myth that explains why something happens in nature. Include events that could not happen in real life.

Name ______________________ Date ______________ Grade

QUIZ Unit 4 • Chapter 3

A. ➤ Vocabulary: Choose the correct answer. *(20 points: 4 points each)*

1. Language structure is ____.
   a. how a word is spelled
   b. how a word is pronounced
   c. the words or sentences around a word
   d. how a word is used in a sentence

2. I love vegetables. My favorite food is ensalada. Ensalada most likely means ____.
   a. chicken
   b. bread
   c. salad
   d. pie

3. Mi hermana, Cristina, and I bought a gift for our mother. Mi hermana most likely means ____.
   a. my uncle
   b. my grandmother
   c. my sister
   d. my brother

4. The *s* in snow is pronounced like the *s* in ____.
   a. shoe
   b. sail
   c. shower
   d. shine

5. The first sound in shake is pronounced like the first sound in ____.
   a. she
   b. saddle
   c. spirit
   d. sky

B. ➤ Text Structure/Elements of Literature: Read and choose the correct answer. *(32 points: 4 points each)*

"The Village Doctor"

1 When I was young, Dr. Juarez visited my parents in our village. Dr. Juarez ran a famous medical school in Mexico City. He said, "Mr. and Mrs. Ortíz, I believe that your daughter could be a fine doctor one day. I will give her a full scholarship to the medical school. " At first, my parents said, "No, *hija*, we need you to work on the farm." But in the end, they let me go to medical school. That is how I became my village's doctor.

6. "The Village Doctor" is a(n) ____.
   a. autobiographical short story
   b. short fiction narrative
   c. letter
   d. speech

7. "The Village Doctor" uses ____.
   a. third-person point of view
   b. second-person point of view
   c. no point of view
   d. first-person point of view

8. What is the setting of "The Village Doctor"?
   a. a Mexican village
   b. Mexico City
   c. a medical school
   d. a large city

9. Dr. Juarez uses formal language. What does this tell you about his experiences?
   a. He probably never went to school.
   b. He does not know how to read.
   c. He is probably well-educated.
   d. He does not understand Spanish.

Name ________________________________ Date ____________________

QUIZ Unit 4 • Chapter 3 (continued)

10. The main character in the story is ____.
a. Mrs. Ortíz **c.** the writer
b. Mr. Ortíz **d.** Dr. Juarez

11. Mr. and Mrs. Ortíz are ____.
a. part of the doctor's family
b. students at the medical school
c. doctors for the village
d. the writer's parents

12. In autobiographical short stories, authors write about ____.
a. events that actually happened to them
b. events that never happened to them
c. events that actually happened to another person
d. events that happened thousands of years ago

13. In "The Village Doctor," what does the Spanish word *hija* probably mean?
a. son
b. daughter
c. mother
d. father

C. ➤ Reading Strategies: Choose the correct answer. *(12 points: 4 points each)*

14. When you compare a text to your own experiences, you ____.
a. summarize the text using your own words
b. notice how a text is similar to your own life
c. describe the main idea of the text
d. analyze causes and effects

15. Comparing a text to your own experiences helps you to ____.
a. learn new vocabulary words
b. find the verbs in a text
c. better recognize the passive voice
d. better understand text events and characters

16. Suppose you felt sad because your dog ran away. Then you read about a character whose dog ran away. You could infer that the character ____.
a. felt sad **c.** read a book
b. felt happy **d.** wrote a poem

D. ➤ Grammar/Usage: Choose the correct answer. *(16 points: 4 points each)*

17. After is stopped raining, I went for a walk. The dependent clause tells ____.
a. when I went for a walk
b. how I went for a walk
c. where I went for a walk
d. why I went for a walk

18. When Willis got home, he called his friend. What is the dependent clause?
a. got home he
b. his friend called
c. When Willis got home
d. he called his friend

19. While she was watching TV, Marta fell asleep. What is the dependent clause?
a. fell asleep
b. she was watching
c. Marta fell asleep
d. While she was watching TV

20. Before school, I go running. Which word in the dependent clause tells you when something happened?
a. school **c.** go
b. I **d.** before

E. ➤ Writing *(20 points)*

Writing Prompt Write a paragraph about a happy experience that you had. Write in the first-person point of view.

Name ______________________________ Date ______________

Grade

QUIZ Unit 4 • Chapter 4

A. ➤ Vocabulary: Choose the correct answer. *(24 points: 4 points each)*

1. Science terms are ____.
   a. books about science
   b. pictures that show science ideas
   c. scientific experiments
   d. words related to science

2. ____ are important words and definitions that are listed in a textbook.
   a. Glosses
   b. Graphics
   c. Thesauruses
   d. Meanings

3. Photos and drawings are types of ____.
   a. glosses
   b. graphics
   c. contractions
   d. adjectives

4. One way to learn new science terms is to ____.
   a. find details that support the main idea
   b. compare and contrast ideas
   c. use figurative language
   d. look for definitions within the text

5. Mateo's class learned about the life cycle of a butterfly. The word cycle means ____.
   a. a type of reference source to use when reading
   b. a violent storm in which winds move in a circle
   c. a process that begins and ends with the same thing
   d. a vehicle with two wheels that is run by pedaling

6. The cyclone destroyed every house. The word cyclone means ____.
   a. a violent storm in which winds move in a circle
   b. a vehicle with two wheels that is run by a machine
   c. a type of reference source to use when reading
   d. a process that begins and ends with the same thing

B. ➤ Text Structure/Elements of Literature: Read and choose the correct answer. *(20 points: 4 points each)*

"All About Ocelots"

1 Ocelots are a type of wildcat. They live in North America. Ocelots are nocturnal. This means that they sleep during the day. At night, they hunt small animals and birds. Today, ocelots are endangered. This means that the ocelots are dying out. There are only about 120 ocelots left in the wild. People are working hard to save the ocelots.

7. "All About Ocelots" is a(n) ____.
   a. historical nonfiction article
   b. historical fiction narrative
   c. informational text
   d. poem

8. Based on this text, endangered means ____.
   a. dying out
   b. safe from all danger
   c. growing in numbers
   d. completely healthy

9. What information in the text supports the fact that ocelots are nocturnal?
   a. They live in North America and are left in the wild.
   b. They sleep during the day and hunt at night.
   c. They are tracked by people during the day.
   d. They are often confused with other wildcats.

Name ________________________ Date ________________

QUIZ Unit 4 • Chapter 4 *(continued)*

10. What problem is discussed in this text?
- **a.** Ocelots cannot find food to eat.
- **b.** Ocelots are killing too many birds.
- **c.** Ocelots are taking over land.
- **d.** Ocelots are at risk of dying out.

11. A _____ would use drawings and labels to explain the word nocturnal.
- **a.** homophone
- **b.** diagram
- **c.** dictionary
- **d.** simile

C. ➤ Reading Strategies: Read and choose the correct answer. *(16 points: 4 points each)*

12. The _____ is the most important idea in a text.
- **a.** main idea
- **b.** detail
- **c.** definition
- **d.** punctuation

13. The main idea of "All About Ocelots" is _____.
- **a.** ocelots are endangered
- **b.** ocelots are nocturnal
- **c.** people love ocelots
- **d.** small animals are afraid of ocelots

14. Which detail supports the main idea of "All About Ocelots"?
- **a.** Ocelots hunt at night.
- **b.** Ocelots are a type of wildcat.
- **c.** They live in North America.
- **d.** There are only about 120 ocelots left in the wild.

15. Alligators and crocodiles are similar animals. Which detail supports this main idea?
- **a.** Alligators are animals.
- **b.** Crocodiles are similar.
- **c.** They are both reptiles.
- **d.** alligators and crocodiles

D. ➤ Grammar/Usage: Choose the correct answer. *(20 points: 4 points each)*

16. In the active voice, the subject of the sentence _____.
- **a.** does an action
- **b.** changes the action
- **c.** becomes the verb
- **d.** is always plural

17. In the passive voice, the subject of the sentence _____.
- **a.** creates an action
- **b.** receives an action
- **c.** changes to a noun
- **d.** is always singular

18. Sasha enjoys swimming very much. The subject of this sentence is _____.
- **a.** enjoys
- **b.** swimming
- **c.** very
- **d.** Sasha

19. Which sentence is in the passive voice?
- **a.** The door swung open.
- **b.** Ana drew a picture.
- **c.** The cake was baked by Tomas.
- **d.** The store opens at 10:00.

20. Which sentence is in the active voice?
- **a.** Sunlight is needed by all plants.
- **b.** Ernesto bought me a book.
- **c.** Pottery is made in giant ovens.
- **d.** The clock was wound.

E. ➤ Writing *(20 points)*

Writing Prompt Write an informational text about a process you know well. Write the steps of the process in chronological order.

Name ________________________________ Date ____________________ Grade

TEST • Unit 4

A. ➤ Reading

"Ivy Versus the Talent Show"

My Notes

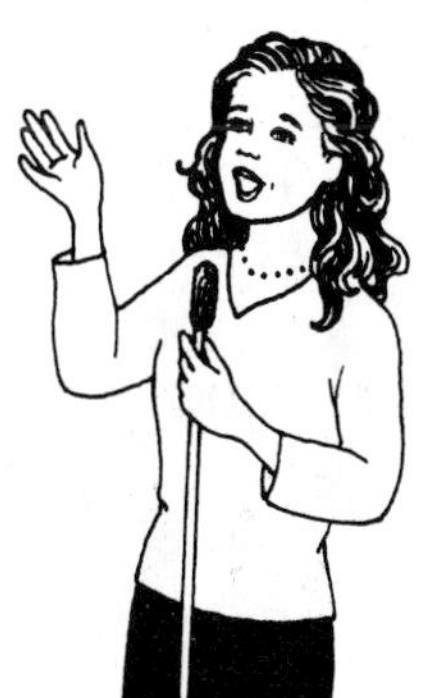

1 Something was going to go terribly wrong.

2 My clock screamed 4:34 A.M., only 13 hours and 26 minutes before the big show! I couldn't sleep because I kept having the same horrible nightmare. In my nightmare, I was standing on a stage and the entire school was in the audience waiting for me to begin my song. Blushing, I grasped the microphone with one hand and timidly raised my other hand to the ceiling. When I opened my mouth to sing, not a sound came out. I tried again, but I could not produce a single note. I stood there, frozen in my spot, embarrassed and afraid as the room spun and the audience laughed at me.

3 I told myself it was only a nightmare, but I lay awake until I had to get up for school. I got dressed slowly, wishing I could find a way to get out of this predicament. I walked to the kitchen and found my favorite breakfast, scrambled eggs, on the table. I read the note that was next to my plate—"Ivy, *mi cara,* I am so excited about the big talent show tonight!" I looked unhappily at my breakfast, too nervous to eat.

4 The morning raced by quickly, and at lunch my friends talked excitedly about the talent show. Susan was going to play the piano and Eric was going to perform magic tricks. I tried to pay attention as Eric practiced his tricks for us, but I kept thinking that I had made a big mistake. How could I have thought I could sing in front of the whole school?

5 Finally, it was time for the show. Waiting nervously behind the stage, I heard Principle Wolf announce, "Now Ivy will sing a song she composed herself!" The audience clapped, and I sluggishly walked on stage, suddenly feeling very scared.

6 I grabbed the microphone, sheepishly raised my other hand, and began to sing. To my amazement, I was singing beautifully! When I finished, the audience cheered loudly and my mother and friends whistled. I bowed and walked offstage. What a relief!

Name ______________________ Date ______________

TEST • Unit 4 (continued)

B. ➤ Reading Comprehension
(20 points: 2 points each)

1. Ivy has a nightmare because she _____.
   - **a.** is worried about passing a test
   - **b.** watched a scary movie the night before
   - **c.** is worried about performing in a talent show
   - **d.** feels guilty about yelling at her friend

2. Who is playing the piano in the talent show?
   - **a.** Susan
   - **b.** Ivy's mother
   - **c.** Eric
   - **d.** Ivy

3. Who is the speaker in the story?
   - **a.** Susan
   - **b.** Principle Wolf
   - **c.** Ivy's mother
   - **d.** Ivy

4. From the ending, you know that the word relief in paragraph 6 means _____.
   - **a.** a feeling of anxiety because of bad weather
   - **b.** a feeling of calm after a difficult time
   - **c.** a beautiful song
   - **d.** a flat, green field

5. From what you know about Ivy, you can conclude that she _____.
   - **a.** is great at math and science
   - **b.** likes to ride her bike after school
   - **c.** is uncomfortable in front of large groups of people
   - **d.** prefers writing poetry instead of singing

6. What do Susan and Eric have in common?
   - **a.** They are both playing the piano in the talent show.
   - **b.** Neither of them knows Ivy.
   - **c.** They are both performing in the talent show.
   - **d.** They are both afraid to perform in the talent show.

7. Which event is most likely to happen next in the reading?
   - **a.** Ivy and her mother celebrate by going out for a special treat.
   - **b.** Ivy continues to worry about performing in the talent show.
   - **c.** Ivy's mother looks disappointed in Ivy.
   - **d.** Ivy's mother's car runs out of gas.

8. What does the picture in the reading represent?
   - **a.** Ivy's singing performance
   - **b.** Ivy's nervousness
   - **c.** the principal's announcement
   - **d.** the audience's clapping

9. Ivy finds it hard to pay attention to Eric because she _____.
   - **a.** does not like magic tricks
   - **b.** is thinking about what to wear that evening
   - **c.** is having a conversation with Susan
   - **d.** is anxious about what will happen that evening

10. The reading begins and ends with an image of Ivy on stage. The author does this to show that _____.
    - **a.** Ivy's nightmare comes true
    - **b.** Ivy should not have worried about the talent show
    - **c.** Ivy wants to be a singer when she grows up
    - **d.** Eric and Susan like Ivy because she is kind

Name ______________________________ Date ______________________

C. ➤ Reading Strategies: Choose the correct answer. *(10 points: 2 points each)*

11. What mental image do you most likely form after reading about Ivy's nightmare?
  a. a young boy hitting a tennis ball
  b. a happy father holding his son
  c. a scared girl standing on a stage
  d. an elderly woman sitting on a park bench

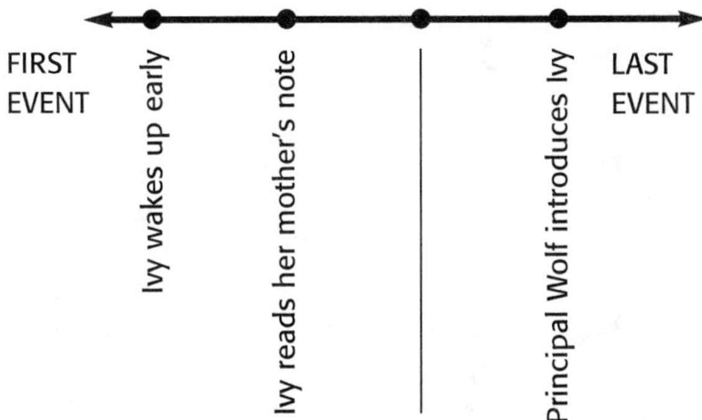

12. Which event best completes the time line above?
  a. Ivy is distracted all day at school.
  b. The audience cheers after Ivy sings.
  c. Ivy has a terrible nightmare.
  d. Ivy gets dressed slowly.

13. Based on paragraph 4 and your own experiences, you can tell that Susan and Eric felt ____ about performing in the talent show.
  a. nervous
  b. angry
  c. excited
  d. confused

14. What is the main idea of paragraph 2?
  a. Ivy is upset because she is not performing in the talent show.
  b. Ivy is scared that she will perform badly in the talent show.
  c. Ivy wakes up late for school.
  d. Ivy remembers a real time when she was embarrassed.

15. Which detail tells you that Ivy sings well in the talent show?
  a. Ivy's mother cooks Ivy's favorite breakfast.
  b. Ivy walks on stage slowly.
  c. Eric performs magic tricks in the talent show.
  d. The audience claps and whistles loudly.

D. ➤ Elements of Literature: Choose the correct answer. *(10 points: 2 points each)*

16. Which of these clues foreshadows that Ivy might be nervous before the talent show?
  a. Ivy had a nightmare about the singing at the talent show.
  b. Ivy's mother left a note saying that she was excited about the talent show.
  c. Principle Wolf announced that Ivy would sing.
  d. Ivy sang amazingly well when it was her turn.

17. "Ivy Versus the Talent Show" is a(n) ____.
  a. informational text
  b. historical nonfiction article
  c. autobiographical short story
  d. science fiction story

Name ______________________________ Date ____________________

TEST • Unit 4 *(continued)*

18. Based on what she writes in the note, Ivy's mother probably ____.

a. thinks that Ivy does not sing well
b. would rather go to the movies than to the talent show
c. is upset because Ivy did not clean her room
d. cares about Ivy very much

19. Which sentence from the reading contains an example of personification?

a. I bowed and walked offstage.
b. My clock screamed 4:34 A.M., only 13 hours and 26 minutes before the big show!
c. I walked to the kitchen and found my favorite breakfast, scrambled eggs, on the table.
d. When I opened my mouth to sing, not a sound came out.

20. "Ivy Versus the Talent Show" is autobiographical and is written in the first-person point of view. This means that ____

a. the author is the narrator
b. the narrator is someone other than the author
c. the events are made up
d. the characters are made up

E. ➤ Vocabulary: Choose the correct answer. *(10 points: 2 points each)*

21. In paragraph 2, the vivid verb blushing helps you understand that Ivy feels ____.

a. tired
b. hungry
c. embarrassed
d. determined

compose /kəm' poʊz/ *v.* **1** to put together with care, esp. writings **2** to create art, esp. music or poetry **3** to calm oneself **4** to make by combining different things

22. Which definition of the word compose most closely matches the meaning of composed in paragraph 5?

a. definition 1
b. definition 2
c. definition 3
d. definition 4

23. In paragraph 1, the contraction couldn't is made up of the words ____.

a. could and not
b. can and not
c. could and will
d. he and is

24. The word microphone in paragraph 1 comes from the Greek word *phōnē*. This means "voice." From this information, you know that a microphone is a ____.

a. machine that cooks food more quickly than an oven
b. small animal with shiny, brown fur
c. type of rough paper
d. tool that makes a person's voice louder

25. In her note in paragraph 3, Ivy's mother calls Ivy *mi cara*, which is an Italian phrase. From the context of the note, *mi cara* probably means ____.

a. her shoe
b. my dear
c. the egg
d. our house

Name ______________________ Date ______________

TEST • Unit 4 *(continued)*

F. ➤ Grammar/Usage: Choose the correct answer. *(10 points: 2 points each)*

26. Which sentence contains a comparative adjective?
a. Rosario is the smartest person in class.
b. The water is way too cold!
c. It is windier today than it was yesterday.
d. She painted a picture of the snowy field.

27. Which of the underlined verbs is an irregular past tense verb?
a. I <u>looked</u> unhappily at my breakfast, too nervous to eat.
b. I <u>bowed</u> and walked off stage.
c. I <u>tried</u> again, but I could not produce a single note.
d. I read the note that <u>was</u> next to my plate.

28. When I opened my mouth to sing, not a sound came out. In this sentence, the dependent clause begins with the word ____.
a. When
b. I
c. not
d. sound

29. The story was written by Mrs. Chang. This sentence ____.
a. contains a contraction
b. is in the passive voice
c. is a dependent clause
d. is in the active voice

30. The car was chased by the dog. Which shows the active voice of this sentence?
a. The car chased the dog.
b. The dog was chased by the car.
c. The dog chased the car.
d. The dog likes to chase cars.

G. ➤ Writing Conventions: Choose the correct answer. *(10 points: 2 points each)*

31. The phone rang at 6:00. Another way to write 6:00 is ____.
a. six oclock
b. six' oclock
c. sixoclock
d. six o'clock

32. Which sentence uses correct capitalization?
a. Ivy's mother speaks Italian.
b. I know how to read spanish.
c. That book is written in english.
d. In India, many people speak hindi.

33. In many texts, words from other languages are written in ____.
a. boldface
b. cursive
c. italics
d. lowercase

34. <u>Cacti</u> are plants that grow in the desert. <u>Cacti</u> is the plural form of ____.
a. cackle
b. cobble
c. cactus
d. center

35. Which word has the long *a* sound?
a. tile
b. ball
c. album
d. mistake

Name ______________________________ Date ____________________

TEST • Unit 4 *(continued)*

H. ➤ Editing: Read and choose the correct answer. *(10 points: 2 points each)*

> (1) The entire family enjoyed this relaxing vacation. (2) When Ariela was young, her family often gone to Florida for vacation. (3) They stayed in a fancy hotel on the beach. (4) Ariela liked going to Florida because she was able to see her friend, Paula, who lived there. (5) Ariela and Paula spent all day swimming in the ocean—they couldn't get enough of it! (6) At night, Ariela's family sometimes went to their favorite restaurant and then took a walk.

36. For a more logical order, sentence 1 should _____.
- **a.** move after sentence 3
- **b.** move to the end of the paragraph
- **c.** move after sentence 5
- **d.** stay where it is

37. What change should you make to sentence 2?
- **a.** change ***When*** to ***How***
- **b.** change ***her*** to ***she***
- **c.** change ***gone*** to ***went***
- **d.** make no change

38. What change should you make to sentence 4?
- **a.** change ***because*** to ***but***
- **b.** change ***her*** to ***his***
- **c.** change ***freind*** to ***friend***
- **d.** make no change

39. What change should you make to sentence 5?
- **a.** change ***spent*** to ***spend***
- **b.** change ***ocean*** to ***Ocean***
- **c.** change ***couldnt*** to ***couldn't***
- **d.** make no change

40. What change should you make to sentence 7?
- **a.** change ***At*** to ***In***
- **b.** change the period to a comma after ***night***
- **c.** change ***their*** to ***thier***
- **d.** make no change

I. ➤ Writing *(20 points)*

> **Writing Prompt** Summarize your favorite story or movie. Use your own words to describe the characters and events. Your summary should be three paragraphs long. Use the Planning Guide to help you write.

Planning Guide

- ❑ In the first paragraph, tell the name of the story or movie. Also describe what the story or movie is mostly about.
- ❑ In the second paragraph, tell the characters' names and what they are like.
- ❑ In the third paragraph, describe two major events in the story or movie. Why are these events important to the story?

Name ______________________ Date ______________ Grade

QUIZ Unit 5 • Chapter 1

A. ➤ Vocabulary: Choose the correct answer. *(20 points: 4 points each)*

1. Making note cards of new words can help you _____.
- **a.** remember the words' meanings
- **b.** use context clues
- **c.** use a reference aid
- **d.** understand main ideas

2. The suffix *-ment* could be added to which of these words?
- **a.** happiest
- **b.** butcher
- **c.** agree
- **d.** coloring

3. The suffix *-ment* changes _____.
- **a.** verbs into nouns
- **b.** verbs to adverbs
- **c.** nouns to verbs
- **d.** nouns to adjectives

4. The patient received good _____.
- **a.** treater
- **b.** treatment
- **c.** treating
- **d.** treat

5. We made a _____ to finish the job.
- **a.** commit
- **b.** committed
- **c.** committer
- **d.** commitment

B. ➤ Text Structure/Elements of Literature: Read and choose the correct answer. *(20 points: 4 points each)*

"Benito Juarez"

Benito Juarez lived from 1806 to 1872. He was the president of Mexico from 1861 to 1863. He was also president from 1867 to 1872. He did whatever he felt was good for the people of Mexico. During his presidency, people were able to live by the constitution. Juarez is considered one of the greatest heroes in Mexican history. Juarez deserved to be president because he helped the Mexican people.

6. "Benito Juarez" is a _____.
- **a.** biography
- **b.** play
- **c.** poem
- **d.** fable

7. A biography _____.
- **a.** tells how to do something
- **b.** compares two different stories
- **c.** tells a story about a real person's life
- **d.** tells an imaginary story

8. A biography often uses _____ to order events.
- **a.** chronology
- **b.** people and places
- **c.** compare and contrast
- **d.** main idea

9. Which sentence sounds most conversational?
- **a.** I will not tolerate bad behavior.
- **b.** I will not allow bad behavior.
- **c.** I will not accept bad behavior.
- **d.** I don't put up with bad behavior.

Name ________________________________ Date ____________________

QUIZ Unit 5 • Chapter 1 *(continued)*

10. Which sentence from "Benito Juarez" sounds most conversational?
- **a.** Benito Juarez lived from 1806 to 1872.
- **b.** He was the president of Mexico from 1861 to 1863 and 1867 to 1872.
- **c.** During his presidency, people were able to live by the constitution.
- **d.** Juarez deserved to be president because he helped the Mexican people.

C. ➤ Reading Strategies: Choose the correct answer. *(20 points: 4 points each)*

11. To make an inference is to _____.
- **a.** use context clues to understand word meanings
- **b.** predict what the text will be about
- **c.** use the text and your experiences to make an educated guess
- **d.** summarize the information in the text

12. Maria makes cakes for a living. You can infer that Maria is a _____.
- **a.** butcher
- **b.** baker
- **c.** teacher
- **d.** waitress

13. Julia smiled when she looked at her report card. You can infer that _____.
- **a.** Julia is helpful
- **b.** Julia needs to study more
- **c.** Julia's favorite subject is math
- **d.** Julia received good grades

14. As the sun was rising, Julio was driving to work. You can infer that the time of day is _____.
- **a.** evening
- **b.** afternoon
- **c.** noon
- **d.** early morning

15. Michael's old pants were too small. You can infer that _____.
- **a.** Michael's pants were brown
- **b.** Michael's pants were two years old
- **c.** Michael is an old man
- **d.** Michael has grown

D. ➤ Grammar/Usage: Choose the correct answer. *(20 points: 4 points each)*

16. Simple past tense verbs describe an action that _____.
- **a.** will happen
- **b.** already happened
- **c.** is happening
- **d.** may happen

17. Last week, Joe _____ himself a new sweater.
- **a.** buys
- **b.** buyer
- **c.** buying
- **d.** bought

18. Yesterday, Susan _____ a letter from her friend.
- **a.** received
- **b.** is receives
- **c.** will receive
- **d.** receiving

19. Which verb is irregular?
- **a.** looked
- **b.** danced
- **c.** cleaned
- **d.** ate

20. Which verb is regular?
- **a.** asked
- **b.** bit
- **c.** drew
- **d.** sat

E. ➤ Writing *(20 points)*

Writing Prompt Write a biography about a person who has made an important change in his or her life. The person should be someone you know.

Name ______________________ Date ______________ Grade

QUIZ Unit 5 • Chapter 2

A. ➤ Vocabulary: Choose the correct answer. *(20 points: 4 points each)*

1. Word squares can help you _____.
   - **a.** remember the meaning of new words
   - **b.** make new words
   - **c.** find the meaning of new words
   - **d.** read new words

2. The suffix *-or* can be added to which of these words?
   - **a.** parking
   - **b.** act
   - **c.** movie
   - **d.** best

3. The suffix *-or* changes _____.
   - **a.** verbs into nouns
   - **b.** verbs into adverbs
   - **c.** nouns into verbs
   - **d.** nouns into adjectives

4. The _____ makes many important decisions.
   - **a.** governor
   - **b.** gove
   - **c.** governing
   - **d.** governly

5. What does the suffix *-or* mean?
   - **a.** in a certain direction
   - **b.** an important activity
   - **c.** a person who does something
   - **d.** from a certain place

B. ➤ Text Structure/Elements of Literature: Read and choose the correct answer. *(28 points: 4 points each)*

"Hadrian's Wall"

1 The Romans invaded Britain in A.D. 43. The Picts of Britain did not want to be conquered, so they attacked the Romans. Hadrian, the Roman emperor, ordered a wall to be built to keep the Picts away. It was called Hadrian's Wall. Roman soldiers guarded the forts along the wall for more than 100 years. The Roman soldiers left Britain in A.D. 383.

6. "Hadrian's Wall" is a _____.
   - **a.** biography
   - **b.** play
   - **c.** historical narrative
   - **d.** speech

7. Which event happened first in "Hadrian's Wall"?
   - **a.** A wall was built.
   - **b.** The Roman soldiers left Britain.
   - **c.** The Picts did not want to be conquered.
   - **d.** The Romans invaded Britain.

"Graduation Day"

1 Congratulations to the graduating class. I am honored to be a part of this celebration. When I look at your class, I feel you are ready to continue to learn and develop new skills. You are valuable members of this community. I wish you the best in everything that you do.

8. "Graduation Day" is a speech. A speech _____.
   - **a.** explains how to do something
   - **b.** tells about an important time in history
   - **c.** presents ideas out loud to an audience
   - **d.** tells an imaginary story

9. A direct address uses the pronouns _____.
   - **a.** *we* and *us*
   - **b.** *I* and *me*
   - **c.** *it* and *they*
   - **d.** *he* and *she*

10. Speakers often repeat words in a speech _____.
    - **a.** to explain more about events
    - **b.** to create a rhythm that excites the audience
    - **c.** to correct their pronunciation
    - **d.** to test the audience

Name ________________________________ Date ____________________

QUIZ Unit 5 • Chapter 2 *(continued)*

11. Two important features of a speech are ____.
    - a. repetition and the speaker's voice
    - b. figurative language and order
    - c. grammar and chronology
    - d. commands and metaphors

12. "The Graduation" will most likely make the reader feel ____.
    - a. happy
    - b. angry
    - c. embarrassed
    - d. sad

C. ➤ Reading Strategies: Choose the correct answer. *(16 points: 4 points each)*

13. When you summarize, you ____.
    - a. use context clues to understand word meanings
    - b. predict what the text will be about
    - c. tell the most important ideas of a text
    - d. explain all the information in a text

14. When you paraphrase, you ____.
    - a. compare and contrast two texts
    - b. make a graphic organizer of a text
    - c. tell the most important ideas of a text
    - d. restate a text in your own words

15. Sam's favorite animal is a monkey. He goes to the zoo on Saturdays to see the animals, especially the monkeys. Which statement is the best summary of these sentences?
    - a. Sam loves many different animals.
    - b. Sam loves monkeys.
    - c. Monkeys live in the zoo.
    - d. The zoo is open on Saturday.

16. Joe cleans his bedroom because it is dirty. First, he picks up all of his clothes. Then he makes his bed. Last, he dusts the furniture. Which statement is the best summary of this story?
    - a. Joe has a dirty bedroom.
    - b. Joe picks up his clothes.
    - c. Joe cleans his room.
    - d. Joe makes his bed.

D. ➤ Grammar/Usage: Choose the correct answer. *(16 points: 4 points each)*

17. An infinitive ____.
    - a. takes the action of a verb
    - b. describes an action
    - c. is a person, place, or thing
    - d. contains the word *to,* plus a verb

18. A verb ____.
    - a. describes a noun
    - b. describes an action
    - c. is a person, place, or thing
    - d. contains the word *to,* plus a verb

19. Angela asked her boss if she could leave work early. Which is the object of the sentence?
    - a. Angela
    - b. asked
    - c. boss
    - d. to leave

20. The library is a great place to study. Which is the infinitive of the sentence?
    - a. library
    - b. is
    - c. place
    - d. to study

E. ➤ Writing *(20 points)*

Writing Prompt Think of a person who you believe is a good role model for others. Write a speech explaining why others should follow his or her example.

Name ______________________________ Date ______________

Grade

QUIZ Unit 5 • Chapter 3

A. ➤ Vocabulary: Choose the correct answer. *(24 points: 4 points each)*

1. Which is an example of a text feature?
  a. setting
  b. italics
  c. question mark
  d. plot

2. Text features often ____.
  a. highlight the meaning of new words
  b. make new words
  c. confuse the meaning of new words
  d. are included to look interesting

3. The root word *grat* means ____.
  a. pleasing
  b. not
  c. before
  d. two

4. Which of the following can be added to the root word *grat* to make a word?
  a. grat
  b. ify
  c. rat
  d. ff

5. Barbara feels ____ toward Mr. Chin because he helped her study.
  a. grate
  b. gratitude
  c. congratulate
  d. ungrateful

6. I am ____ that we have an extra day to study.
  a. congratulate
  b. grateful
  c. gratify
  d. graphics

B. ➤ Text Structure/Elements of Literature: Read and choose the correct answer. *(16 points: 4 points each)*

"The Friendship"

1 Matthew and Jacob met on a beach while they were vacationing in Florida. They played together all week. When it was time to go home, they were upset. They would not see each other again. Their parents suggested that they exchange phone numbers and addresses. Now they are adults. The two have remained close friends over the years.

7. "The Friendship" ____.
  a. describes a beach in Florida
  b. tells a story that could really happen
  c. persuades people to play in the sand
  d. tells a story that could never happen

8. Motivation is the ____.
  a. reason for doing something
  b. main event in a story
  c. result of doing something
  d. problem in a story

9. In "The Friendship," what motivated Matthew and Jacob to play together?
  a. They disliked each other.
  b. They liked each other.
  c. They wanted to see each other again.
  d. They exchanged phone numbers and addresses.

10. In "The Friendship," what motivated Matthew and Jacob to exchange information?
  a. They met each other on vacation.
  b. They were close friends.
  c. Their parents made them.
  d. They wanted to keep in touch.

Name ______________________________ Date ______________________

QUIZ Unit 5 • Chapter 3 *(continued)*

C. ➤ Reading Strategies: Choose the correct answer. *(20 points: 4 points each)*

11. To make a prediction is to ____.
- **a.** use context clues to understand word meanings
- **b.** compare characters in a text
- **c.** guess what will happen in a text
- **d.** summarize the information in a text

12. What is the best way to make a prediction?
- **a.** Read the text word for word.
- **b.** Use text clues and experiences.
- **c.** Ask someone to help you.
- **d.** Use text features.

13. The sun is shining. The children are swimming. Some people are wearing shorts. You can predict that the season is ____.
- **a.** winter
- **b.** spring
- **c.** summer
- **d.** fall

14. The title of a story is "A Big Decision." What do you predict the story will be about?
- **a.** deciding which car to buy
- **b.** a family eating together
- **c.** how to bake a cake
- **d.** planning a party

15. The family was very tired after a long day at the zoo. Mom gave the children a bath and read them a bedtime story. What can you predict will happen next?
- **a.** The children will play a game.
- **b.** Mom will make dinner.
- **c.** The children will fall asleep.
- **d.** The family will draw zoo animals.

D. ➤ Grammar/Usage: Choose the correct answer. *(20 points: 4 points each)*

16. A conjunction ____.
- **a.** has a subject and a verb
- **b.** joins two clauses
- **c.** describes a noun
- **d.** is an action word

17. The conjunction so that usually signals a ____.
- **a.** result
- **b.** time
- **c.** place
- **d.** reason

18. Which uses the conjunction so that correctly?
- **a.** I study hard so that I get good grades.
- **b.** Jim thinks so that he knows everything.
- **c.** The coat so that I bought is too small.
- **d.** I cleaned up the mess so that you made.

19. Which uses the conjunction so that correctly?
- **a.** The baby cried loudly so that his diaper was wet.
- **b.** Basketball is a sport so that many enjoy.
- **c.** The best speller won the contest so that he studied.
- **d.** I ran fast so that I could win the race.

20. Which uses the conjunction so that correctly?
- **a.** Marty saved his money so that he could buy a new house.
- **b.** Hamburgers are a food so that many people enjoy.
- **c.** My goal is so that I have a good job.
- **d.** I can't believe so that Adriana is moving away.

E. ➤ Writing *(20 points)*

Writing Prompt Write a true story about an unforgettable time or event in your life.

Name ______________________________ Date ______________ Grade

QUIZ Unit 5 • Chapter 4

A. ➤ Vocabulary: Choose the correct answer. *(24 points: 4 points each)*

1. The shoes are ____ small for me.
- **a.** two
- **b.** too
- **c.** to
- **d.** toe

2. It is ____ house.
- **a.** their
- **b.** there
- **c.** thare
- **d.** they're

3. Which of the following uses the underlined word correctly?
- **a.** The hot son shined brightly in the sky.
- **b.** It took me an our to drive home.
- **c.** I have one son and two daughters.
- **d.** I need to wash hour dirty clothes.

4. The suffixes *-ible* and *-able* mean ____.
- **a.** having the skill to do something
- **b.** the result of an activity
- **c.** the process of doing something
- **d.** having a certain quality

5. Which root can you add the suffix *-able* to?
- **a.** open
- **b.** value
- **c.** jar
- **d.** green

6. He is ____ of writing very well.
- **a.** disabled
- **b.** capable
- **c.** ability
- **d.** writable

B. ➤ Text Structure/Elements of Literature: Read and choose the correct answer. *(20 points: 4 points each)*

"My Story"

1 I was born on March 3, 1970, in Dallas, Texas. I am of Mexican decent. My family consists of three girls and one boy. We all attended public schools. My father is a fireman and my mother is a nurse. The most important lesson I learned from my parents is to be an honest and loving person.

7. "My Story" is told using ____.
- **a.** first-person narration
- **b.** dialogue
- **c.** third-person point of view
- **d.** the parents' point of view

8. An autobiography tells a story about the life of ____.
- **a.** a family member
- **b.** an important person
- **c.** the author
- **d.** a living person

"Love"

1 Love is a flower
It feels soft
2 Love is a favorite sweater
It becomes familiar
And it is worth experiencing again
and again

9. A metaphor describes something by ____.
- **a.** presenting it as something else
- **b.** using the words like or as
- **c.** giving human qualities to an animal
- **d.** exaggerating something to make a point

Name ________________________________ Date ____________________

QUIZ Unit 5 • Chapter 4 *(continued)*

10. Metaphor is a type of ____.
- **a.** flashback
- **b.** plot
- **c.** figurative language
- **d.** foreshadowing

11. Which line from "Love" is an example of a metaphor?
- **a.** Love is a flower
- **b.** It feels soft
- **c.** It becomes familiar
- **d.** And it is worth experiencing again and again

C. ➤ **Reading Strategies:** Choose the correct answer. *(20 points: 4 points each)*

12. To show how two things are alike is called ____.
- **a.** contrasting
- **b.** connecting
- **c.** comparing
- **d.** summarizing

13. To show how two things are different is called ____.
- **a.** comparing
- **b.** contrasting
- **c.** organizing
- **d.** paraphrasing

14. Which compares apples and lemons?
- **a.** Apples are red. Lemons are yellow.
- **b.** An apple is sweet, but a lemon is not.
- **c.** Apples and lemons are fruit.
- **d.** An apple is round. A lemon is not.

15. Which sentence contrasts dogs and cats?
- **a.** Both are animals and can be pets.
- **b.** A dog barks and a cat meows.
- **c.** Both are brown and feel soft.
- **d.** Dogs and cats are both mammals.

16. Which sentence(s) compare(s) a bedroom to a kitchen?
- **a.** In a bedroom, you sleep. In a kitchen, you eat.
- **b.** Both are places where you cook food.
- **c.** Dressers are in a bedroom. Cabinets are in a kitchen.
- **d.** Both are rooms that can be found in a house.

D. ➤ **Grammar/Usage:** Choose the correct answer. *(16 points: 4 points each)*

17. Superlative adjectives compare ____.
- **a.** a subject and a verb
- **b.** three or more verbs
- **c.** a pronoun and a noun
- **d.** three or more nouns

18. Ron is the ____ boy in his entire class.
- **a.** more taller
- **b.** tall
- **c.** most tallest
- **d.** tallest

19. George is the ____ person I know.
- **a.** most creative
- **b.** creator
- **c.** more creativer
- **d.** creatives

20. That movie was ____ I have ever seen.
- **a.** frightening
- **b.** the most frightening
- **c.** most frightening
- **d.** the frighteningest

E. ➤ **Writing** *(20 points)*

Writing Prompt Write a poem about your life. Include at least one metaphor.

Name ______________________ Date ____________

Grade

TEST • Unit 5

A. ➤ Reading

The Noble Cause of Freedom

1 I have always liked to read about our nation's government and history. I especially enjoy reading about events such as the War for Independence. I also like to read about heroes such as George Washington.

2 Washington was a hero at the Battle of Trenton in New Jersey. "Victory or Death!" he shouted to his men as he crossed the icy Delaware River. He then quickly defeated the surprised troops on the other side. Washington had nerves of steel.

3 I respected Washington's courage in the face of danger. Yet I did not understand the real reason why he had taken the risks that he had. He had not risked his life simply to beat the other side. In my mind, I knew this for certain.

4 I also respected the courage of the soldiers who fought in the Revolutionary War. These men had given up their homes and families to fight on cold battlefields. But once again, what motivated these young soldiers? Why did they choose to face death time and time again? I did not discover the answers to my questions until November 1863.

5 It was a cold November day in Gettysburg, Pennsylvania. Like hundreds of other Pennsylvanians, including our governor, I had traveled to Gettysburg to hear President Abraham Lincoln. He had come to town to dedicate a new cemetery. The cemetery was built to honor the many soldiers who had died at the Battle of Gettysburg.

6 I was only fifteen at the time. The words Lincoln spoke that day will be with me forever. In a sad, yet forceful voice, Lincoln proclaimed in his Gettysburg Address:

7 "We have come to dedicate a portion of [the battlefield], as a final resting place for those who here gave their lives . . . [so that] the nation might live."

8 Lincoln continued in a powerful voice. It carried to the far ends of the cemetery. These men died, he said, so that this nation "shall have a new birth of freedom."

9 The president made it clear to me that the soldiers at Gettysburg had died for the noble cause of freedom. It was then that I also understood why countless other Americans—leaders or ordinary soldiers—had risked their lives in other battles, at other times in history. That day, I truly learned the meaning of Washington's words, "Victory or Death!"

My Notes

TEST • Unit 5 (continued)

B. ➤ Reading Comprehension: Choose the correct answer. *(20 points: 2 points each)*

1. Who is the narrator of the story?
   a. George Washington
   b. Abraham Lincoln
   c. a Revolutionary War soldier
   d. none of the above

2. What battle did Lincoln talk about in his speech?
   a. the Battle of Gettysburg
   b. the Battle of Trenton
   c. the Battle of the Delaware River
   d. the Battle of Washington

3. Where does the narrator of the story live?
   a. New Jersey
   b. Pennsylvania
   c. Delaware
   d. Virginia

4. What is the main idea of paragraph 3?
   a. The narrator does not respect Washington's courage.
   b. The narrator does not understand why Washington had taken certain risks.
   c. The narrator believes that Washington took risks to gain medals.
   d. The narrator believes that Washington was not very brave.

5. Which statement from the story is an opinion?
   a. Washington fought in the War for Independence.
   b. I respected Washington's courage in the face of danger.
   c. I was only fifteen at the time.
   d. Lincoln gave the Gettysburg Address.

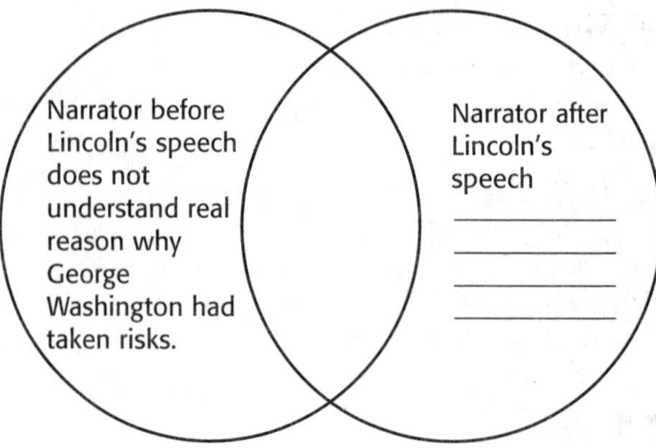

6. Use the Venn Diagram to show how the narrator's feelings changed. How does the narrator's understanding of George Washington change after hearing Lincoln's speech?
   a. The narrator believes George Washington is still fighting.
   b. The narrator is confused about who is George Washington.
   c. The narrator thinks George Washington will soon visit.
   d. The narrator knows why George Washington took certain risks.

7. What was the purpose of the narrator's visit to Gettysburg?
   a. to visit the site of the Battle of Trenton
   b. to visit relatives
   c. to listen to Lincoln give a speech
   d. to listen to Washington give a speech

8. How old was the narrator when he wrote this story?
   a. 15
   b. 12
   c. 10
   d. The story does not give this information.

TEST • Unit 5 *(continued)*

9. The narrator learned that soldiers died for the cause of ____.
- **a.** victory
- **b.** noble
- **c.** freedom
- **d.** courage

10. Which word did the narrator use to describe Lincoln's voice?
- **a.** happy
- **b.** tearful
- **c.** proud
- **d.** powerful

C. ➤ **Reading Strategies:** Choose the correct answer. *(10 points: 2 points each)*

11. From paragraph 1, you can infer that—
- **a.** The narrator likes to play sports.
- **b.** The narrator enjoys learning about science.
- **c.** The narrator is interested in World War I.
- **d.** The narrator enjoys learning about the past.

12. Which of the following is a paraphrase of paragraph 6?
- **a.** The narrator was very young when he heard Lincoln speak.
- **b.** The narrator will always remember listening to Lincoln's Gettysburg Address.
- **c.** Lincoln had a powerful voice.
- **d.** The narrator will be at Gettysburg forever.

13. Which of the following is an accurate summary of paragraph 2?
- **a.** Washington became a hero at the Battle of Trenton.
- **b.** The Battle of Trenton was fought in New Jersey.
- **c.** Washington shouted "Victory or Death."
- **d.** The Delaware River was icy.

14. Which paragraphs explain why the narrator respected Washington and the soldiers who fought in the Revolutionary War?
- **a.** 1 and 2
- **b.** 2 and 3
- **c.** 3 and 4
- **d.** 4 and 5

15. What can you infer from the last sentence in paragraph 4?
- **a.** The narrator was born sometime after 1863.
- **b.** The narrator was 15 when he or she wrote the story.
- **c.** The narrator was born during the Revolutionary War.
- **d.** The narrator was 15 in 1863.

D. ➤ **Elements of Literature:** Choose the correct answer. *(10 points: 2 points each)*

16. Which sentence contains figurative language?
- **a.** I respected Washington's courage in the face of danger.
- **b.** I have always liked to read about our nation's history.
- **c.** I also respected the courage of the regular soldiers who had fought in the Revolutionary War.
- **d.** The words Lincoln spoke that day will be with me forever.

17. Which sentence contains a metaphor?
- **a.** Lincoln continued in a powerful voice.
- **b.** That day, I truly learned the meaning of Washington's words, "Victory or Death!"
- **c.** Washington had nerves of steel.
- **d.** It was a cold day in Gettysburg, Pennsylvania.

TEST • Unit 5 *(continued)*

18. According to the narrator, what motivated George Washington to risk his life at the Battle of Trenton?
- **a.** medals
- **b.** recognition
- **c.** freedom
- **d.** courage

19. Which visual would help you understand the phrase *in the face of danger* in paragraph 3?
- **a.** a picture of a very mean face
- **b.** a picture of Washington's troops landing behind him
- **c.** a picture of Washington with a dangerous face
- **d.** a picture of an army of enemy troops facing Washington

20. What was Lincoln's possible motivation for giving the Gettysburg Address?
- **a.** He wanted to honor the soldiers who had died.
- **b.** He wanted to comfort the families of the soldiers who had died.
- **c.** He wanted to tell everyone that the soldiers had died for a noble cause.
- **d.** all of the above

E. ➤ Vocabulary: Read and choose the correct answer. *(10 points: 2 points each)*

21. In paragraph 1, the word government means _____.
- **a.** to rule or control
- **b.** official elected as the head of a state
- **c.** system of ruling
- **d.** the way someone rules

22. In paragraph 5, the word governor means _____.
- **a.** to rule or control
- **b.** person who rules or governs
- **c.** system of ruling
- **d.** the way that someone rules

23. Which sentence uses the underlined word correctly?
- **a.** Soldiers chose too leave their families to fight.
- **b.** They wanted two win the war for many reasons.
- **c.** Women, to, fought in the war.
- **d.** Soldiers risk their lives to win a war.

24. The people felt that he was honorable in his work as president. Honorable means _____.
- **a.** refusing to help others in your work
- **b.** not respecting the people around you
- **c.** showing a sense of what is right
- **d.** feeling bad about what has been done

25. The people who listened to President Lincoln were thankful that he had helped dedicate the cemetery. Which could be used in place of thankful?
- **a.** gratify
- **b.** congratulate
- **c.** grateful
- **d.** gratification

F. ➤ Grammar/Usage: Choose the correct answer. *(10 points: 2 points each)*

26. Which sentence uses the correct conjunction?
- **a.** He dedicated the cemetery so that people would remember the soldiers who had died for our country.
- **b.** He dedicated the cemetery and people would remember the soldiers who had died for our country.
- **c.** He dedicated the cemetery but people would remember the soldiers who had died for our country.
- **d.** He dedicated the cemetery or people would remember the soldiers who had died for our country.

Name ____________________ Date ____________________

TEST • Unit 5 *(continued)*

27. Which sentence has an irregular simple past tense verb?
- **a.** The group walked to the battlefield.
- **b.** I sent her my new address.
- **c.** My brother answered the phone.
- **d.** The hikers traveled a great distance.

28. Which sentence has an irregular simple past tense verb?
- **a.** The class had a good time at the zoo.
- **b.** I rehearsed my lines in the play last night.
- **c.** My brother talked with his friend for an hour.
- **d.** We looked at the sunset.

29. Which sentence has a superlative adjective?
- **a.** He is shorter than I am.
- **b.** Dogs are usually larger than cats.
- **c.** Radar is the smallest dog I have ever seen.
- **d.** We live in a large apartment on Central Street.

30. Which sentence has a verb, an object, and an infinitive?
- **a.** History is an interesting subject.
- **b.** The boy ran all the way home.
- **c.** The governor asked the President to come.
- **d.** I am a very careful person.

G. ➤ Writing Conventions: Choose the correct answer. *(10 points: 2 points each)*

31. Which sentence has a spelling mistake?
- **a.** He was unusually quiet this evening.
- **b.** She is a very qwick runner.
- **c.** Their parents controlled what they could watch on TV.
- **d.** The clip was fastened to the coat.

32. Which sentence has a spelling mistake?
- **a.** I was really right about the result of that game.
- **b.** You were wrong to stay out so late.
- **c.** I promise that I will rite you a letter soon.
- **d.** School has always been easy for me.

33. Which sentence has a punctuation mistake?
- **a.** I was born on January 21 1988.
- **b.** I am going to go on vacation in March.
- **c.** We have two cats, and their bowls are in the kitchen.
- **d.** My friend, Laura, was born on February 1, 1989.

34. Which sentence has a capitalization mistake?
- **a.** The Declaration of Independence is a great document.
- **b.** He works for Mr. Lopez's company.
- **c.** Lincoln gave his gettysburg address in 1863.
- **d.** Tim and Mason belong to the drama club.

35. Which sentence has a punctuation mistake?
- **a.** The Civil War was fought mainly in the South.
- **b.** The author, John T Raymond, is from Atlanta.
- **c.** I lost the dog's collar at the park.
- **d.** Jasmine, Terry, and Manuel attended the party.

Name ______________________ Date ______________

H. ➤ Editing: Read and choose the correct answer. *(10 points: 2 points each)*

African Americans in the Civil War

(1) When the Civil War broke out, many African Americans from the North volunteer. (2) At first they're help was refused. (3) Finally, African American units were formed. (4) It had white officers. (5) Before the war was over, more than 200,000 African Americans had fighted for the Union. (6) More than 100 of the soldiers later will became officers.

36. What change should you make to sentence 1?
a. change ***Civil War*** to ***civil war***
b. change ***Americans*** to ***americans***
c. change ***volunteer*** to ***volunteered***
d. make no change

37. What change should you make to sentence 2?
a. change ***At*** to ***On***
b. change ***they're*** to ***their***
c. change ***refused*** to ***refusal***
d. make no change

38. What change should you make to sentence 4?
a. change ***It*** to ***They***
b. change ***white*** to ***White***
c. change ***officers*** to ***officer***
d. make no change

39. What change should you make to sentence 5?
a. change ***200,000*** to ***20,0000***
b. change ***Americans*** to ***americans***
c. change ***had fighted*** to ***had fought***
d. make no change

40. What change should you make to sentence 6?
a. change ***100*** to ***1,00***
b. change ***soldiers*** to ***soldier***
c. change ***will became*** to ***became***
d. make no change

I. ➤ Writing *(20 points)*

Writing Prompt Write a three-paragraph newspaper story. Tell about an event that happened recently in your town or school. Write a headline for your story. Use the Planning Guide to help you write.

Planning Guide
- ❑ Write in the third person. Use pronouns in your writing.
- ❑ Tell the most important information first.
- ❑ Answer who, what, when, why, where, and how questions in your story.
- ❑ When you finish writing, proofread your work.

Name ______________________ Date ______________ Grade

QUIZ Unit 6 • Chapter 1

A. ➤ Vocabulary: Choose the correct answer. *(32 points: 4 points each)*

1. Connotative meanings are ____.
   a. meanings found in the dictionary
   b. the spelling of the word
   c. feelings attached to a word
   d. words that are connected to each other

2. Which sentence gives the denotative definition of lemonade?
   a. Lemonade is my favorite drink.
   b. Lemonade cools you off on hot days.
   c. Lemonade is a drink made from lemons, sugar, and water.
   d. Lemonade is a refreshing drink.

3. They ____ look very happy about arriving late. Which contraction completes the sentence?
   a. it's
   b. hadn't
   c. don't
   d. isn't

4. ____ late for the meeting. Which contraction best completes the sentence?
   a. Can't
   b. You're
   c. Aren't
   d. Don't

5. ____ time to go to the library. Which contraction best completes the sentence?
   a. Its
   b. I'll
   c. It's
   d. Didn't

6. What two words form the contraction you'll?
   a. you and are
   b. you and would
   c. are and not
   d. you and will

7. What two words form the contraction it's?
   a. is and not
   b. it and is
   c. I and am
   d. I and is

8. What two words form the contraction I'd?
   a. I and is
   b. I and would
   c. I and can
   d. I and will

B. ➤ Text Structure/Elements of Literature: Read and choose the correct answer. *(16 points: 4 points each)*

"The Mystery"

Scene 1

SETTING: *Classroom*

ALICE (*running into the room, out of breath*): Mrs. Applebee? (*She looks around for Mrs. Applebee, then addresses the group of students in the corner*) Have you seen Mrs. Applebee? (*The students shake their heads to indicate "no." Alice turns to run out the door and runs into Jasper as he enters the room*).
JASPER (*surprised and irritated*): Hey! Slow down. What's your hurry?
ALICE: I've got to find Mrs. Applebee. It's an emergency!

9. Alice and Jasper are ____ in the play.
   a. settings
   b. scenes
   c. characters
   d. stage directions

10. When does this part of the play take place?
    a. Scene 1
    b. Scene 2
    c. Scene 3
    d. Scene 4

Name ______________________________ Date ____________________

QUIZ Unit 6 • Chapter 1 *(continued)*

11. What is the setting of the play?
a. a playground
b. the gym
c. a classroom
d. the principal's office

12. How do the students respond to Alice's question?
a. They talk to her.
b. They ignore her.
c. They pass her a note.
d. They shake their heads.

C. ➤ Reading Strategies: Choose the correct answer. *(16 points: 4 points each)*

13. The order in which things happen is called ____.
a. recall
b. timeline
c. narrative
d. chronology

14. Matt woke up. He showered and dressed. He grabbed an apple to eat as he headed out of the door. Which did Matt do first?
a. went to school
b. ate breakfast
c. woke up
d. went home

15. Zelma wrote an essay about her vacation. She shared her story with the class. She later shared it with her family. What did Zelma do first?
a. She wrote about her vacation.
b. She left school.
c. She shared her story with her class.
d. She shared her story with her family.

16. First Sean makes his bed. Then he puts away anything that is out of place. Next he dusts his dressers. Finally, he checks under the bed for lost items. What does Sean do after he puts things away?
a. He makes his bed.
b. He dusts his dressers.
c. He vacuums the room.
d. He checks under the bed.

D. ➤ Grammar/Usage: Choose the correct answer. *(16 points: 4 points each)*

17. I ____ hard all evening.
a. has studied **c.** have study
b. have studied **d.** has study

18. He ____ his ankle two times.
a. is twister **c.** has twisted
b. twisting **d.** have twist

19. Someone ____ the lawn.
a. have watered **c.** have watering
b. has watered **d.** waters

20. The children ____ patiently.
a. is waits **c.** has wait
b. have waited **d.** waiter

E. ➤ Writing *(20 points)*

Writing Prompt Write a play about someone being persuaded to do something. Use chronology.

Name ______________________ Date ______________ Grade

QUIZ Unit 6 • Chapter 2

A. ➤ Vocabulary: Choose the correct answer. *(24 points: 4 points each)*

1. A word that has the opposite meaning of another word is called a(n) _____.
   a. definition
   b. context clue
   c. antonym
   d. prefix

2. It was strange to see a deer in my backyard. An antonym for strange is _____.
   a. amazing
   b. unusual
   c. better
   d. common

3. Mr. Langone was our permanent music teacher. The antonym for permanent is _____.
   a. regular
   b. reading
   c. temporary
   d. different

4. The English language often borrows words from _____.
   a. verbs
   b. English
   c. other languages
   d. suffixes

5. When I traveled to South America, it was the first time I had ever eaten a mango. The word mango means a kind of _____.
   a. fruit that grows in warm places
   b. homemade tomato sauce
   c. frozen dessert
   d. lemon-lime drink

6. Hannie had never been to school before, and was excited about going off to kindergarten. The word kindergarten means a _____.
   a. club for teen-aged children
   b. class for young children
   c. camp for children who play tennis
   d. group where parents meet other parents

B. ➤ Text Structure/Elements of Literature: Read and choose the correct answer. *(32 points: 4 points each)*

"The Chocolate River"

1 I went down to the park behind my house early on Saturday morning. I thought I'd sit by the river and watch the ducks for awhile. Well, I got a big surprise! As I walked down to the water, I thought it looked very muddy. It was brown and soupy looking. When I got right to the edge of the river, I couldn't believe what I saw—groups of people drinking from it! Somehow overnight the river had turned into a pool of thick, rich chocolate! I felt as though I was in a dream, and I hoped I wouldn't wake up too soon.

7. "The Chocolate River" is a _____.
   a. biography
   b. rhyming poem
   c. fictional story
   d. drama

8. Where does "The Chocolate River" take place?
   a. in a park
   b. in a backyard
   c. in a city
   d. in a chocolate factory

9. "The Chocolate River" is about _____.
   a. a group of people who go to the park
   b. ducks that swim in a river
   c. people resting in a park
   d. a surprise at the river

10. When does "The Chocolate River" take place?
    a. on a Saturday morning
    b. on a Sunday afternoon
    c. an evening night
    d. a summer night

Name ______________________ Date ______________

QUIZ Unit 6 • Chapter 2 *(continued)*

11. First-person point of view is when _____.
- **a.** the action in the story is at its highest
- **b.** a character in a story tells the story
- **c.** the characters use dialogue in a story
- **d.** the story ends on a happy note

12. In "The Chocolate River," the speaker shares his or her feelings and thoughts by using the words _____.
- **a.** he and him
- **b.** she and her
- **c.** I and me
- **d.** they and them

13. Which group of words from the passage is an example of the first-person point of view?
- **a.** I got a big surprise
- **b.** it looked very muddy
- **c.** groups of people drinking from it
- **d.** pool of thick, rich chocolate

14. In the first-person point of view, the reader _____.
- **a.** knows what the writer or narrator is thinking
- **b.** knows what all of the characters are thinking
- **c.** knows what a few of the characters are thinking
- **d.** does not know what the narrator is thinking

C. ➤ Reading Strategies: Choose the correct answer. *(12 points: 4 points each)*

15. Writers do not always tell the readers everything directly. Sometimes the reader has to _____.
- **a.** find facts
- **b.** give an opinion
- **c.** draw conclusions
- **d.** read details

16. It is Gina's first day of camp. She is standing alone and not talking to anyone. You can draw the conclusion that Gina has _____.
- **a.** been away from home before
- **b.** made friends easily
- **c.** never been to camp
- **d.** a fear of swimming

17. Mrs. Reyes is packing her clothes in a suitcase. You can conclude Mrs. Reyes is _____.
- **a.** at the movies
- **b.** meeting friends for lunch
- **c.** going to school
- **d.** going on vacation

D. ➤ Grammar/Usage: Choose the correct answer. *(12 points: 4 points each)*

18. The Garzas are packing. _____ leaving for vacation in the morning.
- **a.** There
- **b.** They're
- **c.** Their
- **d.** They will

19. This will be the first time the twins have gone to a movie. It is _____ first time.
- **a.** they are
- **b.** their
- **c.** there
- **d.** they're

20. Did Ramona go for a walk? When I came home, she wasn't _____.
- **a.** there
- **b.** their
- **c.** they're
- **d.** they are

E. ➤ Writing *(20 points)*

Writing Prompt Write a description of a place that you think is special. Use words that will help your reader picture what the place looks and feels like.

Name ______________________ Date ______________ Grade

QUIZ Unit 6 • Chapter 3

A. ➤ Vocabulary: Choose the correct answer. *(24 points: 4 points each)*

1. Correct _____ is saying a word as it should sound.
- **a.** definition
- **b.** pronunciation
- **c.** vocabulary
- **d.** context

2. You can find the pronunciation of a word in a(n) _____.
- **a.** thesaurus
- **b.** dictionary
- **c.** synonym finder
- **d.** encyclopedia

3. If you know where a word comes from, you know its _____.
- **a.** derivation
- **b.** pronunciation
- **c.** spelling
- **d.** meaning

4. If you know the word tendere means to stretch in Latin, then you know that _____.
- **a.** English words with *tendere* in them might be used in Latin
- **b.** there are no English words with *tendere* in them
- **c.** English words that come from *tendere* might have something to do with stretching
- **d.** English words do not use Latin parts

5. Since tendere means to stretch, the word extend probably means to _____.
- **a.** make longer
- **b.** make shorter
- **c.** give back
- **d.** take from someone

6. Since tendere means to stretch, the word attend probably means to _____.
- **a.** make a plan
- **b.** stay for a length of time
- **c.** leave
- **d.** forget a promise

B. ➤ Text Structure/Elements of Literature: Read and choose the correct answer. *(32 points: 4 points each)*

"The Cocoon Opens"

1 For many months, Opal had been carefully watching the tree outside her house. Every time she looked, she noticed something small, gray, and soft sticking to the side of the tree. She did not want to brush it off, because she had a feeling that something might be going on inside the fluffy sack. One day, as she was sitting and watching the tree, something wonderful happened. She watched in amazement as the cocoon opened up. Out came a bright black and orange butterfly.

7. "The Cocoon Opens" is a(n) _____.
- **a.** drama
- **b.** adventure
- **c.** mystery
- **d.** realistic fiction

8. What is the real place in "The Cocoon Opens"?
- **a.** a park
- **b.** the tree
- **c.** a garden
- **d.** Opal's house

9. What usually happens at the beginning of a plot?
- **a.** The title of the story is given.
- **b.** The author is introduced.
- **c.** The characters and setting are introduced.
- **d.** The ending of the story is revealed.

10. What happens at the beginning of "The Cocoon Opens"?
- **a.** Opal sees a butterfly come out of its cocoon.
- **b.** Opal goes into her house.
- **c.** Opal watches a tree.
- **d.** Opal touches a fluffy sack.

Name ______________________________ Date ____________________

QUIZ Unit 6 • Chapter 3 *(continued)*

11. What usually happens in the middle of a plot?
- **a.** The characters go away.
- **b.** The characters try to solve a problem.
- **c.** The author restarts the story.
- **d.** The author quickly ends the story.

12. What is the problem in "The Cocoon Opens"?
- **a.** Opal wanted to know what was in the fluffy sack on the tree.
- **b.** Opal had trouble planting her tree.
- **c.** Opal could not remember where the fluffy sack was.
- **d.** Opal forgot to look out for the butterfly.

13. What usually happens at the end of a plot?
- **a.** The author tells how he or she chose the ending.
- **b.** The author leads the reader to predict what happens next.
- **c.** The characters begin to act like other characters in the story.
- **d.** The characters solve the problem that was given in the story.

14. What happens at the end of "The Cocoon Opens"?
- **a.** Opal watches a butterfly hide under a cocoon.
- **b.** Opal catches a butterfly.
- **c.** Opal looks carefully at a tree, but nothing happens.
- **d.** Opal watches as a butterfly comes out of its cocoon.

C. ➤ Reading Strategies: Choose the correct answer. *(12 points: 4 points each)*

15. When you make inferences, you use text evidence, your knowledge, and your ____.
- **a.** experiences
- **b.** problems
- **c.** writing skills
- **d.** own predictions

16. Mari ran down the street in her gym clothes and sneakers. She shouted, "We won! We won!" You can infer that Mari ____.
- **a.** is the first person to finish a race
- **b.** is on a team that won a game
- **c.** is getting ready to start a library project
- **d.** is one of the best spellers in her class

17. The stars were shining in the moonlit sky. You can infer that it is ____.
- **a.** morning
- **b.** nighttime
- **c.** noon
- **d.** breakfast time

D. ➤ Grammar/Usage: Choose the correct answer. *(12 points: 4 points each)*

18. Use a ____ to connect two different parts of a sentence.
- **a.** conjunction
- **b.** noun
- **c.** pronoun
- **d.** synonym

19. Thomasina is going to the shopping mall, ____ her older brother is driving her there.
- **a.** until
- **b.** who
- **c.** and
- **d.** that

20. Paulo had to do his laundry ____ he had no more clean shirts.
- **a.** if
- **b.** where
- **c.** over
- **d.** because

E. ➤ Writing *(20 points)*

Writing Prompt Write a short fiction story. Make up a character. Describe a problem that he or she needs to solve.

Name ______________________________ Date ______________ Grade

QUIZ Unit 6 • Chapter 4

A. ➤ Vocabulary: Choose the correct answer. *(24 points: 4 points each)*

1. The words preserve, recycling, air, and water are related because they all have to do with the ____.
   - **a.** sun
   - **b.** streams
   - **c.** environment
   - **d.** sky

2. The words elevator and washing machine should be grouped in a category about ____.
   - **a.** machines
   - **b.** clothing
   - **c.** buildings
   - **d.** animals

3. The word industrial has something to do with ____.
   - **a.** recycling things
   - **b.** using the sun to heat things
   - **c.** making things
   - **d.** keeping things

4. The prefix *co–* means ____.
   - **a.** one
   - **b.** all alone
   - **c.** together with
   - **d.** many things

5. Coworkers are people who ____.
   - **a.** build things
   - **b.** work together
   - **c.** draw art
   - **d.** work alone

6. A coauthor is a writer who ____.
   - **a.** works alone
   - **b.** works in an office
   - **c.** works with another writer to create a book
   - **d.** creates a book about another person

B. ➤ Text Structure/Elements of Literature: Read and choose the correct answer. *(32 points: 4 points each)*

"Let's Raise Money"

1 Last year, our class was not able to take any trips. The school did not have enough money to send us anywhere—not to a museum, a play, or a baseball game. But this year, we can start early and raise enough money for our own trips. We can have a brownie sale and collect enough money to plan a great trip. All we have to do is a little work, and we can have a great adventure.

7. The author wrote "Let's Raise Money" to ____ readers.
   - **a.** annoy
   - **b.** inform
   - **c.** entertain
   - **d.** persuade

8. What problem is explained in the text?
   - **a.** The class had a brownie sale.
   - **b.** The school did not have enough money last year.
   - **c.** The school will collect the money.
   - **d.** The class can plan a trip.

9. What detail is an example of the problem in the text?
   - **a.** The class could not take any trips last year.
   - **b.** The class does not want to go to a museum.
   - **c.** The class does not want to raise money.
   - **d.** The class cannot have a brownie sale.

10. What solution does the author give for the problem?
    - **a.** go to a museum
    - **b.** plan a trip
    - **c.** raise money
    - **d.** start school earlier

Name ________________________________ Date ____________________

QUIZ Unit 6 • Chapter 4 *(continued)*

11. The author's _____ is the reason why an author writes.
a. information **c.** plot
b. story **d.** purpose

12. When an author tries to persuade the reader, he or she tries to get the reader to _____.
a. be interested in a story
b. understand information
c. agree with the author
d. enjoy a story

13. In "Let's Raise Money," the author wants people to _____.
a. do a little work to raise money
b. help build a new school building
c. buy brownies
d. pay for their own trips

14. The author tries to persuade the reader in "Let's Raise Money" by saying that _____.
a. other schools have brownie sales
b. going to baseball games is the perfect way to raise money
c. raising enough money can lead to a great adventure
d. museums are fun places to spend money

C. ➤ Reading Strategies: Choose the correct answer. *(12 points: 4 points each)*

15. The best way to understand the main ideas of a text is to _____.
a. make inferences **c.** give opinions
b. summarize **d.** predict

16. A father and his children are in the kitchen. They are making cookies. They will sell the cookies in the evening. Which summarizes these sentences?
a. They are getting ready to leave home.
b. They went to the grocery store for ingredients.
c. They are preparing for a bake sale.
d. They spilled flour on the kitchen floor.

17. Nadia just returned from an exciting trip to another country. She saw elephants and monkeys in the jungle. Which summarizes these sentences?
a. She spent a lot of money on her trip.
b. She visited the jungle and saw lots of animals.
c. She traveled on two airplanes to get to the jungle.
d. She took a lot of pictures on her trip.

D. ➤ Grammar/Usage: Choose the correct answer. *(12 points: 4 points each)*

18. The word will shows that something is going to happen in the _____.
a. author's mind **c.** reader's mind
b. past **d.** future

19. When she goes to school tomorrow, Georgia _____ past my house.
a. will walk **c.** walked
b. walks **d.** was walking

20. Next year, my parents _____ our house a different color.
a. paint **c.** painted
b. will paint **d.** were painting

E. ➤ Writing *(20 points)*

Writing Prompt Write an informational text to describe what your town will look like in the future. Use the future tense.

Name ______________________________ Date ____________________ Grade

TEST • Unit 6

A. ➤ Reading

Something Funny Is Cooking in the Kitchen: Scene I

My Notes

Setting: *A kitchen*

At Rise: Charlie *is sitting at the kitchen table with his parents. He is shaking his head.*

1 Charlie's Mom (*Worried*): Charlie, you haven't eaten.

2 Charlie's Dad: Are you okay?

3 Charlie (*In sort of a haze*): I'm fine. I just had a strange dream. Go ahead and go to work. I will leave for school in a few minutes.

4 (Charlie's *parents leave, saying "Goodbye" and "Call us if you need us."*)

5 Charlie: Well, that was a weird dream. (*Stands up.*)
(*At this point, a container of milk on the table starts talking.*)

6 Milk: Yeah, it was just a dream. You know what they say — don't cry over spilled milk!

7 Charlie: What was that?!?

8 Milk: It's okay, buddy. It's just us, now.

9 Charlie (*Shocked*): Are you talking to me?

10 Milk: Is there someone else here?

11 Charlie: But you're a container of milk!!

12 Milk: Yes, I am. Cool, smooth, and good for you. And only 1% fat!

13 Charlie: But you're talking! Like in my dream!

14 Milk: Hey, pal — that was no dream. I've been talking for years. I don't know why you never heard me before!

15 (Charlie *looks around and sees the doors of the cabinets open. An egg beater, a blender, and a coffee maker start making machine-like noises. Above him, the ceiling fan starts moving.*)

16 Ceiling Fan (*Excitedly*): Me too, buddy!

17 Blender (*A little annoyed*): Frankly, I wondered why it took you so long. I'm not exactly the quiet type!

18 Coffee Maker (*Cheerful*): Oh, Blender! Calm down.

19 Blender (*Still annoyed*): Excuse me. I have been stuck in that cabinet for months — I don't get used every day like you!!

20 Coffee Maker: Well, maybe that's why I have such a *bubbly* personality!

21 Egg Beater (*Yelling*): Oh, give me a break!!

22 Charlie (*To the milk container, in great confusion*): Who's *that*?!?

23 Milk: Oh, that's just the egg beater. He's getting a little whipped up, because the coffee maker is always laughing.

24 Coffee Maker: The other machines are all jealous of me, because I'm happy all the time!

25 Charlie: Is this some kind of joke?

26 Milk (*Trying to calm him down a little*): No, Charlie. We've been here all along. Just think, you can tell all your friends about us!

27 Charlie: They'd never believe me. (*Starts talking to himself*) Well, maybe I'm dreaming. Maybe I'm *not.* But I still have to get ready for school — maybe everything will be normal later.

28 Coffee Maker: Of course, dear. Everything will perk up, I promise!

29 Charlie: Very funny. Well, one thing is for sure — I have watched too many cartoons late at night! (*Starts to walk out the door.*)

30 Ceiling Fan (*Calling after him*): Have a cool day!

Name ______________________________ Date ______________________

B. ➤ Reading Comprehension: Choose the correct answer. *(20 points: 2 points each)*

1. Why does Charlie say, "I have watched too many cartoons late at night"?
   a. He thinks he's getting too old to be watching cartoons.
   b. He thinks he stayed awake too late last night.
   c. He thinks cartoons made him have a strange dream.
   d. He thinks there are other programs on television that are better than cartoons.

2. Why do you think this play is titled *Something Funny Is Cooking in the Kitchen?*
   a. because it has a lot of humor
   b. because something is cooking
   c. because it is in the kitchen
   d. because strange things are happening

3. What information does the scene give you about Charlie's parents?
   a. They both go to school.
   b. They are a little worried about Charlie.
   c. They are afraid that Charlie will be late for school.
   d. They work in an office.

4. The picture with the reading helps you to know what about Milk?
   a. Milk is shy.
   b. Milk acts like a real person.
   c. Milk has no friends.
   d. Milk likes Charlie.

5. What do you learn about Coffee Maker from the play?
   a. Coffee Maker is cheerful.
   b. Coffee Maker is unhappy.
   c. Coffee Maker is tired of living in a kitchen cabinet.
   d. Coffee Maker is one of Milk's best friends.

6. Which of the following characters in the play is not happy?
   a. Milk
   b. Coffee Maker
   c. Blender
   d. Ceiling Fan

7. Why does Charlie decide he will leave for school?
   a. He hopes when he returns later on, things will be more normal.
   b. He has finished eating breakfast.
   c. He forgot to tell his parents something.
   d. He is angry at the talking ceiling fan.

8. How would you describe the tone that the author is trying to create in this scene?
   a. angry
   b. sad
   c. funny
   d. tired

9. What is interesting about Coffee Maker saying "I have such a *bubbly* personality"?
   a. When coffee is heating up, it smells good.
   b. When coffee is heating up, it makes people happy.
   c. When coffee is heating up, it looks dark brown.
   d. When coffee is heating up, it makes bubbles.

10. Charlie's parents leave the kitchen to _____.
    a. drop off Charlie at school
    b. get away from the talking kitchen appliances
    c. go to work
    d. go back to sleep

Name ______________________ Date ______________________

TEST • Unit 6 (continued)

C. ➤ Reading Strategies: Choose the correct answer. *(10 points: 2 points each)*

11. Which line tells you when the scene takes place?
- **a.** Are you talking to me?
- **b.** Charlie, you haven't eaten.
- **c.** I will leave for school in a few minutes.
- **d.** You know what they say — don't cry over spilled milk!

12. How do you know that something unusual is going on in Charlie's kitchen?
- **a.** Things are talking that don't usually talk.
- **b.** His parents decide to leave.
- **c.** He eats his breakfast.
- **d.** The ceiling fan is moving.

13. What inferences can you make about the appliances?
- **a.** They are made of metal.
- **b.** They cannot all talk.
- **c.** They have been talking to Charlie's parents for years.
- **d.** They can be happy or angry.

14. How would you describe Charlie's feelings at the end of the scene?
- **a.** He feels excited and can't wait to tell his friends about what happened.
- **b.** He feels nervous and hopes that things will return to normal later in the day.
- **c.** He feels sad that he doesn't have more time to stay at home.
- **d.** He feels angry that some of the appliances have not been nicer to him.

15. Which spoke first in the play?
- **a.** Ceiling Fan
- **b.** Egg Beater
- **c.** Blender
- **d.** Coffee Maker

D. ➤ Elements of Literature: Choose the correct answer. *(10 points: 2 points each)*

16. Which is an example of dialogue?
- **a.** BLENDER (*A little annoyed*):
- **b.** COFFEE MAKER:
- **c.** MILK: Oh, that's just the egg beater.
- **d.** CHARLIE *looks around and sees the doors of the cabinets open.*

17. Which is an example of stage directions?
- **a.** CHARLIE *is sitting at the kitchen table with his parents.*
- **b.** CHARLIE'S DAD: Are you okay?
- **c.** SETTING: *A kitchen*
- **d.** MILK: Hey, pal — that was no dream.

18. What is the main plot of this play?
- **a.** Charlie is worried that his parents work too hard.
- **b.** Charlie has decided to become a better student.
- **c.** Charlie has been watching a lot of television.
- **d.** Charlie has to figure out if he is dreaming.

19. How will Charlie's problem most likely be solved?
- **a.** He will get to school on time.
- **b.** He will see his parents later in the day.
- **c.** He will realize that he was dreaming.
- **d.** He will finish his breakfast.

20. What is the purpose of this play?
- **a.** to inform the audience about something important
- **b.** to persuade the audience to change their minds
- **c.** to entertain the audience with something they will enjoy
- **d.** to ask questions the audience wants answered

TEST • Unit 6 *(continued)*

E. ➤ Vocabulary: Choose the correct answer. *(10 points: 2 points each)*

21. The attitude of Coffee Maker could be described as festive. Festive means _____.
a. strange
b. joyful
c. lazy
d. sad

22. *Something Funny Is Cooking in the Kitchen* describes a morning that is unusual. An antonym for unusual is _____.
a. usual
b. fast
c. unhappy
d. healthy

23. Which pronunciation key helps you to say the word haze correctly?
a. /has/
b. /heiz/
c. /həz/
d. /hæz/

24. An egg beater, a coffee maker, and a blender are all types of _____.
a. food
b. appliances
c. clothing
d. furniture

25. Which word from the play is a contraction?
a. I'm
b. eaten
c. buddy
d. ready

F. ➤ Grammar/Usage: Choose the correct answer. *(10 points: 2 points each)*

26. Which is an example of the present perfect tense?
a. I watch too many cartoons late at night.
b. I will watch too many cartoons late at night.
c. I have watched too many cartoons late at night.
d. I am watching too many cartoons late at night.

27. The other machines are all jealous of me. You could rewrite the sentence as, _____ all jealous of me."
a. "Their
b. "There
c. "There's
d. "They're

28. He's getting a little whipped up, because the coffee maker is always laughing. Which word is a conjunction?
a. He's
b. because
c. always
d. getting

29. Which sentence uses the future tense?
a. I just had a strange dream.
b. Are you talking to me?
c. I will leave for school in a few minutes.
d. Oh, give me a break!

30. Which is an example of the present perfect tense?
a. I was stuck in that cabinet for months.
b. I have been stuck in that cabinet for months.
c. I had been stuck in that cabinet for months.
d. I been stuck in that cabinet for months.

TEST • Unit 6 *(continued)*

G. ➤ Writing Conventions: Choose the correct answer. *(10 points: 2 points each)*

31. Which shows correct punctuation for when a character in a play is about to speak?
- **a.** CHARLIE!
- **b.** CHARLIE,
- **c.** CHARLIE:
- **d.** CHARLIE—

32. Well, maybe I'm dreaming. Maybe I'm *not.* The word not is in italics to ____.
- **a.** tell the reader to say the word more strongly than the other words
- **b.** tell that someone is unsure of what to say next
- **c.** show that a character is confused about where to go next
- **d.** describe a special place that the character would like to visit

33. Which word has the sound /f/ in the middle as in the word different?
- **a.** milk
- **b.** pal
- **c.** egg
- **d.** laughing

34. Which word has a silent letter?
- **a.** know
- **b.** had
- **c.** just
- **d.** down

35. We honor soldiers on Memorial Day. Memorial Day is capitalized because it is ____.
- **a.** the first part of a sentence
- **b.** a holiday
- **c.** someone's birthday
- **d.** someone's name

Name ______________________________ Date ____________________

H. ➤ Editing: Read and choose the correct answer. *(10 points: 2 points each)*

When I Read

(1) When I read, I like to picture the scene in my mind. (2) If the author is writing about a forest, I imagine walking with my friend joseph. (3) We look around and hear the beauty of the green trees, yellow plants, and small animals. (4) I try to hear the crunch of pine needles under our feet, but we walk and talk. (5) I think about the fresh, outdoor smell of pine all around me. (6) I need to pack a sleeping bag the next time I go camping in the forest. (7) Then I have a real picture of what the author is writing about.

36. What change should you make to sentence 1?
- **a.** change ***When*** to ***How***
- **b.** change ***like*** to ***likes***
- **c.** change ***in*** to ***on***
- **d.** make no change

37. What change should you make to sentence 2?
- **a.** change ***If*** to ***So***
- **b.** change ***friend*** to ***freind***
- **c.** change ***joseph*** to ***Joseph***
- **d.** make no change

38. What change should you make to sentence 3?
- **a.** change ***hear*** to ***see***
- **b.** change ***hear*** to ***taste***
- **c.** change ***hear*** to ***smell***
- **d.** make no change

39. What change should you make to sentence 4?
- **a.** change ***try*** to ***tried***
- **b.** change ***under*** to ***above***
- **c.** change ***but*** to ***while***
- **d.** make no change

40. For a more logical order, sentence 6 should be ____.
- **a.** the title of the story
- **b.** the last line in the story
- **c.** taken out of the story
- **d.** left where it is

I. ➤ Writing *(20 points)*

Writing Prompt Describe your most prized possession. Tell why it is important to you. Use the Planning Guide to help you write.

Planning Guide
- ❏ Use descriptive words to help your reader picture your possession.
- ❏ Write in the first-person point of view.
- ❏ Check your spelling, punctuation, and capitalization.
- ❏ Write neatly.

Name ______________________ Date ______________ Grade

END-OF-BOOK EXAM

A. ➤ Reading

The Beach

My Notes

1 The beach is like a delicious box of mixed chocolates — you never know what treat you're going to find next. The other day, for example, I spotted a large, mysterious dark patch about 100 yards off shore. At first, I thought it was just the shadow of a cloud over the sea, but the sky was a clear blue.

2 My curiosity took hold of me. I kept staring at the patch, like it was an alien spaceship. Then I saw it move! First it scurried left. Then it darted right. Then in a blink, it rushed toward the beach in a giant swoosh. As the ominous patch edged closer, it glittered like a handful of sunlit diamonds. What in the world could it be? As it drew even closer, I could see that the wiggly mass was not only moving forward, it was moving upward as well! It heaved up for several seconds and then collapsed in a frothy heap.

3 I grabbed my binoculars. When I focused them on the patch, I instantly discovered its mystery. The patch was one of the largest schools of fish I had ever seen! I wonder what other treasure the beach will unveil the next time I visit.

How to Hit a Golf Ball

1 Hitting a golf ball may look difficult, but you can be hitting 200-yard drives in no time if you follow these steps. Remember, if you are left-handed, you will need to reverse some of the steps for the opposite side of your body.

2 First, lay the club in your left palm about two inches from the top of the club. Then place your right hand closely below your left hand. Grip the club gently, as if you were shaking hands.

3 Next, position the ball so that it is lined up with your left heel. Position your feet so that they are spread no wider than your shoulders.

4 Then, take the club back slowly, making sure you do not move your head. Stop when your back is turned directly toward your target. Your weight is now on your right side.

5 Transfer your weight on the downswing to the left side. When you strike the ball, you should be moving forward. Your head should remain still.

6 Remember to follow through on the shot while making sure you end up with the club behind your left shoulder.

Name ______________________ Date ______________

END-OF-BOOK EXAM *(continued)*

B. ➤ Reading Comprehension: Read and choose the correct answer. *(20 points: 2 points each)*

1. In "The Beach," what did the narrator first think the patch was in the water?
   a. a flock of seagulls
   b. a whale
   c. an underwater mountain
   d. the shadow of a cloud

2. In "How to Hit a Golf Ball," which word did the narrator use to describe how you should grip a club?
   a. gently
   b. tightly
   c. loosely
   d. quickly

3. How are the two stories similar?
   a. Both use figurative language.
   b. Both are written in the first person.
   c. Both are written in the second person.
   d. none of the above

4. In "The Beach," what is the main idea of paragraph 3?
   a. The narrator found his or her binoculars.
   b. The narrator discovered that the patch was a large school of fish.
   c. The narrator discovered that sand had covered his blanket.
   d. The narrator discovered a new water mammal.

5. Which statement is an opinion?
   a. Grip the club gently, as if you were shaking hands.
   b. Hitting a golf ball may look difficult, but you can be hitting 200-yard drives in no time.
   c. Lay the club gently in your left palm about two inches from the top of the club.
   d. Transfer your weight on the downswing to the left side.

6. In "How to Hit a Golf Ball," which step must be taken first?
   a. Transfer your weight on the downswing to the left side.
   b. Follow through, making sure you end up with the club behind your left shoulder.
   c. When you strike the ball, you should be moving forward.
   d. Grip the club gently, as if you were shaking hands.

7. In "The Beach," why couldn't the narrator move when he or she first saw the patch?
   a. He or she had leg cramp.
   b. He or she was tired.
   c. He or she was frightened.
   d. He or she was curious.

8. In "The Beach," what did the narrator do to solve the mystery of the patch?
   a. A friend told the author.
   b. The author walked out on a pier.
   c. The author used a pair of binoculars.
   d. The author swam out to the patch.

9. How are the two readings different?
   a. "The Beach" describes an experience, while "How to Hit a Golf Ball" describes a process.
   b. "The Beach" describes a process, while "How to Hit a Golf Ball" tries to persuade.
   c. "The Beach" tries to persuade, while "How to Hit a Golf Ball" tries to influence.
   d. "The Beach" is a narrative, while "How to Hit a Golf Ball" is a speech.

10. In "How to Hit a Golf Ball," what should you do if you are left-handed?
    a. Reverse some steps for the opposite side of your body.
    b. Shake hands with the club.
    c. Position your feet wider than your shoulders.
    d. Carry the clubs on your left side.

Name ______________________________________ Date ____________________________

END-OF-BOOK EXAM *(continued)*

C. ➤ Reading Strategies: Read and choose the correct answer. *(10 points: 2 points each)*

11. In "The Beach," you can infer that ____.
- **a.** the narrator does not like fish
- **b.** the narrator enjoys nature
- **c.** the narrator likes space ships
- **d.** the narrator works with animals

12. Which is an accurate paraphrase of the first sentence in "How to Hit a Golf Ball"?
- **a.** Hitting a golf ball is as easy as it looks.
- **b.** You can learn to hit a golf ball in one easy step.
- **c.** Hitting a golf ball doesn't look easy, but if you follow these steps you can soon be hitting long drives.
- **d.** You will discover that it is difficult to hit a golf ball if you follow these steps.

13. Which is an accurate summary of paragraph 3 in "The Beach"?
- **a.** The author used binoculars to discover that the patch was a large school of fish.
- **b.** The author had a difficult time finding the binoculars.
- **c.** The author was disappointed to discover that the patch was a large school of fish.
- **d.** The author wondered why the school of fish was so large.

14. Which event occurred last in "The Beach"?
- **a.** The author observed a mysterious patch.
- **b.** The author used binoculars to observe the patch.
- **c.** The author noticed that the patch heaved up for several seconds.
- **d.** The author noticed that the sky was cloudless.

15. What conclusion can you draw from "How to Hit a Golf Ball"?
- **a.** Hitting a golf ball is easier than hitting a baseball.
- **b.** Hitting a golf ball is very difficult.
- **c.** Hitting a golf ball correctly requires a good grip.
- **d.** You do not need instructions to play golf well.

D. ➤ Elements of Literature: Read and choose the correct answer. *(10 points: 2 points each)*

16. Which sentence contains figurative language?
- **a.** My curiosity took hold of me.
- **b.** The patch was one of the largest schools of fish I had ever seen!
- **c.** Take the club back slowly, making sure you do not move your head.
- **d.** I grabbed my binoculars.

17. Which sentence is an example of first-person narrative?
- **a.** My favorite place is the beach.
- **b.** I kept staring at the patch, like it was something that had been dropped from the sky.
- **c.** The other day, for example, I spotted a large, mysterious dark patch about 100 yards off shore.
- **d.** all of the above

18. In "The Beach," what character traits does the narrator show?
- **a.** He or she is always angry.
- **b.** He or she is curious.
- **c.** He or she is honest.
- **d.** He or she is mean.

19. What is the purpose of "The Beach"?
- **a.** to inform
- **b.** to persuade
- **c.** to entertain
- **d.** to annoy

Name ______________________ Date ______________________

END-OF-BOOK EXAM *(continued)*

20. How would you describe the mood in reading 1?
   a. suspenseful
   b. sad
   c. happy
   d. gloomy

E. ➤ Vocabulary: Choose the correct answer. *(10 points: 2 points each)*

21. In paragraph 2 of "The Beach," the phrase *in a blink* means ____.
   a. very quickly
   b. very slowly
   c. very lightly
   d. too dark to see

22. In "The Beach," paragraph 2, a good antonym for giant would be ____.
   a. gigantic
   b. tiny
   c. shiny
   d. dark

23. Which sentence uses the word there correctly?
   a. There my best friends.
   b. I want you to know that there going to lose the game.
   c. He is not sure if he wants to stay here or go there.
   d. There bus is leaving now.

24. Which word is formed from the root mystery?
   a. misting
   b. mysterious
   c. myth
   d. math

a•li•en /eɪLiən/ *n.* **1** person who is not a citizen of the country in which he or she lives. *adjective* **2** of another country; foreign. *adjective* **3** entirely different; strange. *noun* **4** an imaginary creature from outer space. *adjective* **5** of or belonging to an imaginary creature from outer space.

25. Look at the dictionary entry for the word alien. Which meaning most closely matches the meaning of alien in paragraph 2 of "The Beach"?
   a. 1
   b. 2
   c. 3
   d. 5

F. ➤ Grammar/Usage: Choose the correct answer. *(10 points: 2 points each)*

26. Which sentence has a vivid verb?
   a. It glittered like a handful of sunlit diamonds.
   b. The fish swam around the shore.
   c. It was swimming quickly.
   d. The shark swam around me.

27. Which sentence is in the future tense?
   a. I am walking home from school.
   b. He won the race.
   c. My sister will create a new poster.
   d. She can go with you.

28. Which sentence uses the passive voice?
   a. The girls think they will pass the test.
   b. Food and water are needed by all people.
   c. The sun creates lots of heat.
   d. They raced to the finish line.

29. Which sentence is correct?
   a. The mall is noisier than usual.
   b. He is happy than his friend.
   c. Mary is busy than she wants to be.
   d. She is the saddest than her sister.

30. Which sentence has a dependent clause?
   a. Biology, history, and English are my favorite subjects.
   b. The twins ran all the way home.
   c. When he reached the finish line, his mom congratulated him.
   d. You should be careful not to spill the ink.

Name ______________________ Date ______________________

END-OF-BOOK EXAM (continued)

G. ➤ Writing Conventions: Choose the correct answer. *(10 points: 2 points each)*

31. Which sentence has a capitalization mistake?
- **a.** His family always eats turkey on thanksgiving.
- **b.** They all gathered around the tree on Christmas.
- **c.** President Lincoln was shot in 1865.
- **d.** I will meet you at the library on Tuesday.

32. Which sentence has a spelling mistake?
- **a.** I have an appointment with the fotografer tomorrow.
- **b.** Please pass me a nife and a fork.
- **c.** The large dog completely destroid our garden.
- **d.** all of the above

33. Which sentence has a word or words that should be in *italics?*
- **a.** "Hola," Marie said to the class. Hola is the Spanish word for hello.
- **b.** "It's time for recess!" she shouted.
- **c.** He thinks it is important to study the Constitution.
- **d.** "Hello," Aaron said to his teacher.

34. Choose the sentence that uses their, they're, or there correctly.
- **a.** There dog is always getting loose.
- **b.** They're the smartest kids in school.
- **c.** Place the book on the shelf over their.
- **d.** Their will be a price to pay for being late.

35. Which sentence has a punctuation error?
- **a.** He will be twenty-three years old in March.
- **b.** Anne was born on November 18, 1990.
- **c.** I am scheduled to take the test on December 12.
- **d.** My daughter was born on October 5 1977.

Name ______________________ Date ______________

END-OF-BOOK EXAM *(continued)*

H. ➤ Editing: Read and choose the correct answer. *(10 points)*

> (1) Sarah and Nadia was looking forward to the big game. (2) Them want their team, the Longfellow Eagles, to beat the Tremper Trojans. (3) The game is scheduled for next week. (4) Sarah and Nadia plan on meeting at the gate the day of the game. (5) Both of them hope to see they're friend Melissa. (6) Her might not be able to attend the game because she was sick last week.

36. What change should you make to sentence 1?
- **a.** change ***Nadia*** to ***nadia***
- **b.** change ***was looking*** to ***are looking***
- **c.** change ***to*** to ***too***
- **d.** make no change

37. What change should you make to sentence 2?
- **a.** change ***Them*** to ***They***
- **b.** change ***want*** to ***wants***
- **c.** change ***to beat*** to ***beating***
- **d.** make no change

38. What change should you make to sentence 3?
- **a.** change ***is*** to ***was***
- **b.** change ***for*** to ***on***
- **c.** change ***week*** to ***weeks***
- **d.** make no change

39. What change should you make to sentence 5?
- **a.** change ***Both*** to ***Any***
- **b.** change ***they're*** to ***their***
- **c.** change ***Melissa*** to ***melissa***
- **d.** make no change

40. What change should you make to sentence 6?
- **a.** change ***Her*** to ***She***
- **b.** change ***might*** to ***won't***
- **c.** change ***because*** to ***but***
- **d.** make no change

I. ➤ Writing *(20 points)*

> **Writing Prompt** Write a poem that is based on one of the themes in this book: mysteries, survival, journeys, cycles, freedom, or visions. Your poem should have at least five stanzas (groups of lines). Use the Planning Guide to help you write.

Planning Guide
- ❑ Choose a theme and brainstorm topics that are of interest to you.
- ❑ Choose one topic and list several details.
- ❑ Use at least one example of figurative language in each stanza.
- ❑ Include sensory words.
- ❑ Check your final draft for spelling, capitalization, and punctuation.
- ❑ Make sure your final draft is written in cursive form and is legible.

Answer Key

Diagnostic Test

A. Vocabulary Meaning

1. c 3. a 5. b
2. b 4. c

B. Word Study

6. b 8. c 10. d
7. d 9. b

C. Reading Comprehension

11. b 15. d 19. c
12. c 16. b 20. c
13. c 17. a
14. c 18. b

D. Reading Stategies

21. a 23. c 25. c
22. c 24. a

E. Grammar/Usage

26. b 28. c 30. c
27. d 29. c

F. Spelling

31. d 33. c 35. c
32. c 34. c

G. Writing

Answers will vary.

H. Writing Conventions

36. b 38. b 40. d
37. d 39. a

Unit 1 Chapter 1 Quiz

A. Vocabulary

1. d 3. b 5. a
2. b 4. c 6. c

B. Text Structure/Elements of Literature

7. d 10. d 13. b
8. a 11. b 14. d
9. b 12. c

C. Reading Strategies

15. a 16. b 17. c

D. Grammar/Usage

18. d 19. c 20. a

E. Writing

Answers will vary.

Unit 1 Chapter 2 Quiz

A. Vocabulary

1. b 3. c 5. b
2. a 4. d 6. d

B. Text Structure/Elements of Literature

7. a 10. d 13. b
8. c 11. d 14. c
9. a 12. a

C. Reading Strategies

15. a 16. c 17. d

D. Grammar/Usage

18. d 19. d 20. c

E. Writing

Answers will vary.

Unit 1 Chapter 3 Quiz

A. Vocabulary

1. b 3. c 5. b
2. a 4. d 6. c

B. Text Structure/Elements of Literature

7. c 10. d 13. a
8. a 11. d 14. c
9. c 12. a

C. Reading Strategies

15. a 16. b 17. d

D. Grammar/Usage

18. d 19. d 20. c

E. Writing

Answers will vary.

Unit 1 Chapter 4 Quiz

A. Vocabulary

1. b 3. c 5. b
2. a 4. d 6. c

B. Text Structure/Elements of Literature

7. c 10. a 13. d
8. b 11. b 14. a
9. c 12. b

C. Reading Strategies

15. c 16. a 17. b

D. Grammar/Usage

18. c 19. d 20. b

E. Writing

Answers will vary.

Unit 1 Chapter 5 Quiz

A. Vocabulary

1. d 3. b 5. a
2. c 4. b 6. c

B. Text Structure/Elements of Literature

7. a 10. d 13. b
8. b 11. b 14. b
9. c 12. a

C. Reading Strategies

15. c 16. d 17. a

D. Grammar/Usage

18. d 19. a 20. b

E. Writing

Answers will vary.

Unit 1 Test

B. Reading Comprehension

1. d 5. d 9. d
2. c 6. b 10. b
3. a 7. a
4. c 8. c

C. Reading Strategies

11. c 13. b 15. d
12. a 14. d

D. Elements of Literature

16. c 18. d 20. b
17. c 19. a

E. Vocabulary

21. d 23. c 25. b
22. a 24. d

F. Grammar/Usage

26. c 28. d 30. d
27. b 29. a

G. Writing Conventions

31. a 33. c 35. c
32. b 34. c

H. Editing
36. a 37. b 38. c 39. d 40. b

I. Writing
Answers will vary.

Unit 2 Chapter 1 Quiz

A. Vocabulary
1. c 2. d 3. b 4. c 5. b

B. Text Structure/Elements of Literature
6. b 7. c 8. b 9. a 10. d 11. a 12. d 13. d 14. b

C. Reading Strategies
15. b 16. b 17. c

D. Grammar/Usage
18. b 19. a 20. d

E. Writing
Answers will vary.

Unit 2 Chapter 2 Quiz

A. Vocabulary
1. a 2. b 3. c 4. c 5. b 6. d 7. c

B. Text Structure/Elements of Literature
8. d 9. c 10. c 11. b 12. b

C. Reading Strategies
13. a 14. a 15. a 16. c

D. Grammar/Usage
17. d 18. a 19. b 20. b

E. Writing
Answers will vary.

Unit 2 Chapter 3 Quiz

A. Vocabulary
1. a 2. a 3. d 4. a 5. b 6. b 7. b

B. Text Structure/Elements of Literature
8. c 9. b 10. a 11. c

C. Reading Strategies
12. b 13. a 14. c 15. a

D. Grammar/Usage
16. a 17. b 18. a 19. b 20. a

E. Writing
Answers will vary.

Unit 2 Chapter 4 Quiz

A. Vocabulary
1. a 2. d 3. a 4. c 5. a

B. Text Structure/Elements of Literature
6. a 7. b 8. a 9. a 10. a 11. b 12. c

C. Reading Strategies
13. b 14. c 15. b 16. b

D. Grammar/Usage
17. b 18. b 19. a 20. a

E. Writing
Answers will vary.

Unit 2 Chapter 5 Quiz

A. Vocabulary
1. d 2. a 3. d 4. c 5. d

B. Text Structure/Elements of Literature
6. b 7. c 8. b 9. a 10. b

C. Reading Strategies
11. b 12. b 13. a 14. b 15. a

D. Grammar/Usage
16. d 17. a 18. a 19. d 20. a

E. Writing
Answers will vary.

Unit 2 Test

B. Reading Comprehension
1. b 2. b 3. a 4. a 5. c 6. a 7. c 8. a 9. b 10. d

C. Reading Strategies
11. c 12. a 13. a 14. d 15. b

D. Elements of Literature
16. c 17. d 18. b 19. c 20. d

E. Vocabulary
21. b 22. c 23. d 24. c 25. c

F. Grammar/Usage
26. d 27. c 28. a 29. d 30. c

G. Writing Conventions
31. a 32. b 33. b 34. c 35. c

H. Editing
36. b 37. a 38. b 39. c 40. b

I. Writing
Answers will vary.

Unit 3 Chapter 1 Quiz

A. Vocabulary
1. b 2. c 3. c 4. c 5. c

B. Text Structure/Elements of Literature
6. a 8. d 10. a
7. a 9. d 11. b

C. Reading Strategies
12. c 14. c
13. b 15. d

D. Grammar/Usage
16. c 18. c 20. b
17. b 19. d

E. Writing
Answers will vary.

Unit 3 Chapter 2 Quiz

A. Vocabulary
1. c 4. d 7. d
2. a 5. b
3. b 6. c

B. Text Structure/Elements of Literature
8. a 10. c 12. c
9. d 11. a

C. Reading Strategies
13. b 14. c 15. a

D. Grammar/Usage
16. d 18. d 20. b
17. c 19. a

E. Writing
Answers will vary.

Unit 3 Chapter 3 Quiz

A. Vocabulary
1. a 4. a 7. b
2. c 5. c
3. b 6. c

B. Text Structure/Elements of Literature
8. b 10. c 12. d
9. d 11. a

C. Reading Strategies
13. b 14. c 15. a

D. Grammar/Usage
16. d 18. b 20. b
17. d 19. c

E. Writing
Answers will vary.

Unit 3 Chapter 4 Quiz

A. Vocabulary
1. c 4. b 7. c
2. a 5. a
3. a 6. b

B. Text Structure/Elements of Literature
8. c 10. c 12. b
9. d 11. a

C. Reading Strategies
13. c 14. d 15. a

D. Grammar/Usage
16. c 18. d 20. a
17. a 19. b

E. Writing
Answers will vary.

Unit 3 Chapter 5 Quiz

A. Vocabulary
1. a 3. c 5. d
2. b 4. c

B. Text Structure/Elements of Literature
6. a 9. a 12. c
7. b 10. b 13. b
8. c 11. d

C. Reading Strategies
14. d 16. b
15. a 17. c

D. Grammar/Usage
18. b 19. d 20. d

E. Writing
Answers will vary.

Unit 3 Test

B. Reading Comprehension
1. b 5. c 9. c
2. c 6. b 10. b
3. a 7. a
4. d 8. b

C. Reading Strategies
11. b 13. a 15. d
12. c 14. d

D. Elements of Literature
16. b 18. b 20. d
17. c 19. a

E. Vocabulary
21. c 23. d 25. a
22. d 24. b

F. Grammar/Usage
26. a 28. b 30. d
27. c 29. c

G. Writing Conventions
31. c 33. a 35. b
32. d 34. c

H. Editing
36. d 38. c 40. a
37. b 39. a

I. Writing
Answers will vary.

Mid-Book Exam

B. Reading Comprehension
1. b 5. d 9. b
2. a 6. a 10. a
3. b 7. d
4. c 8. c

C. Reading Strategies
11. a 13. a 15. c
12. c 14. b

D. Elements of Literature
16. d 18. c 20. d
17. b 19. a

E. Vocabulary
21. a 23. b 25. d
22. c 24. d

F. Grammar/Usage
26. c 28. a 30. d
27. b 29. c

G. Writing Conventions
31. c 33. b 35. c
32. a 34. d

H. Editing
36. b 38. b 40. c
37. b 39. c

I. Writing
Answers will vary.

Unit 4
Chapter 1 Quiz

A. Vocabulary
1. c 4. d 7. d
2. a 5. c
3. b 6. b

B. Text Structure/Elements of Literature
8. a 10. b 12. d
9. d 11. c 13. b

C. Reading Strategies
14. c 15. d 16. b

D. Grammar/Usage
17. a 19. d
18. c 20. b

E. Writing
Answers will vary.

Unit 4
Chapter 2 Quiz

A. Vocabulary
1. b 4. b 7. d
2. d 5. a
3. a 6. d

B. Text Structure/Elements of Literature
8. b 10. d 12. c
9. a 11. c

C. Reading Strategies
13. b 15. d 17. a
14. b 16. b

D. Grammar/Usage
18. c 19. a 20. d

E. Writing
Answers will vary.

Unit 4
Chapter 3 Quiz

A. Vocabulary
1. d 3. c 5. a
2. c 4. b

B. Text Structure/Elements of Literature
6. a 9. c 12. a
7. d 10. c 13. b
8. a 11. d

C. Reading Strategies
14. b 15. d 16. a

D. Grammar/Usage
17. a 19. d
18. c 20. d

E. Writing
Answers will vary.

Unit 4
Chapter 4 Quiz

A. Vocabulary
1. d 3. b 5. c
2. a 4. d 6. a

B. Text Structure/Elements of Literature
7. c 9. b 11. b
8. a 10. d

C. Reading Strategies
12. a 14. d
13. a 15. c

D. Grammar/Usage
16. a 18. d 20. b
17. b 19. c

E. Writing
Answers will vary.

Unit 4 Test

B. Reading Comprehension
1. c 5. c 9. d
2. a 6. c 10. b
3. d 7. a
4. b 8. a

C. Reading Strategies
11. c 13. c 15. d
12. a 14. b

D. Elements of Literature
16. a 18. d 20. a
17. c 19. b

E. Vocabulary
21. c 23. a 25. b
22. b 24. d

F. Grammar/Usage
26. c 28. a 30. c
27. d 29. b

G. Writing Conventions
31. d 33. c 35. d
32. a 34. c

H. Editing
36. b 38. c 40. b
37. c 39. c

I. Writing
Answers will vary.

Unit 5
Chapter 1 Quiz

A. Vocabulary
1. a 3. a 5. d
2. c 4. b

B. Text Structure/Elements of Literature
6. a 8. a 10. d
7. c 9. d

C. Reading Strategies
11. c 13. d 15. d
12. b 14. d

D. Grammar/Usage
16. b 18. a 20. a
17. d 19. d

E. Writing
Answers will vary.

Unit 5
Chapter 2 Quiz

A. Vocabulary
1. a 3. a 5. c
2. b 4. a

B. Text Structure/Elements of Literature
6. c 9. a 12. a
7. d 10. b
8. c 11. a

C. Reading Strategies
13. c 15. b
14. d 16. c

D. Grammar/Usage
17. d 19. c
18. b 20. d

E. Writing
Answers will vary.

Unit 5 Chapter 3 Quiz

A. Vocabulary
1. b 3. c 5. b
2. a 4. a 6. b

B. Text Structure/Elements of Literature
7. b 9. b
8. a 10. d

C. Reading Strategies
11. c 13. c 15. c
12. b 14. a

D. Grammar/Usage
16. b 18. a 20. a
17. d 19. d

E. Writing
Answers will vary.

Unit 5 Chapter 4 Quiz

A. Vocabulary
1. b 3. c 5. b
2. a 4. a 6. b

B. Text Structure/Elements of Literature
7. a 9. a 11. a
8. c 10. c

C. Reading Strategies
12. c 14. c 16. d
13. b 15. b

D. Grammar/Usage
17. d 19. a
18. d 20. b

E. Writing
Answers will vary.

Unit 5 Test

B. Reading Comprehension
1. d 5. b 9. c
2. a 6. d 10. d
3. b 7. c
4. b 8. d

C. Reading Strategies
11. d 13. a 15. a
12. b 14. c

D. Elements of Literature
16. a 18. c 20. d
17. c 19. d

E. Vocabulary
21. c 23. c 25. c
22. b 24. c

F. Grammar/Usage
26. a 28. a 30. c
27. b 29. c

G. Writing Conventions
31. b 33. a 35. b
32. c 34. c

H. Editing
36. c 38. a 40. c
37. b 39. c

I. Writing
Answers will vary.

Unit 6 Chapter 1 Quiz

A. Vocabulary
1. c 4. b 7. b
2. c 5. c 8. b
3. c 6. d

B. Text Structure/Elements of Literature
9. c 11. c
10. a 12. d

C. Reading Strategies
13. d 15. a
14. c 16. b

D. Grammar/Usage
17. b 19. b
18. c 20. b

E. Writing
Answers will vary.

Unit 6 Chapter 2 Quiz

A. Vocabulary
1. c 3. c 5. a
2. d 4. c 6. b

B. Text Structure/Elements of Literature
7. c 10. a 13. a
8. a 11. b 14. a
9. d 12. c

C. Reading Strategies
15. c 16. c 17. d

D. Grammar/Usage
18. b 19. b 20. a

E. Writing
Answers will vary.

Unit 6 Chapter 3 Quiz

A. Vocabulary
1. b 3. a 5. a
2. b 4. c 6. b

B. Text Structure/Elements of Literature
7. d 10. c 13. d
8. b 11. b 14. d
9. c 12. a

C. Reading Strategies
15. a 16. b 17. b

D. Grammar/Usage
18. a 19. c 20. d

E. Writing
Answers will vary.

Unit 6 Chapter 4 Quiz

A. Vocabulary
1. c 3. c 5. b
2. a 4. c 6. c

B. Text Structure/Elements of Literature
7. d 10. c 13. a
8. b 11. d 14. c
9. a 12. c

C. Reading Strategies
15. b 16. c 17. b

D. Grammar/Usage
18. d 19. a 20. b

E. Writing
Answers will vary.

Unit 6 Test

B. Reading Comprehension
1. c 5. a 9. d
2. d 6. c 10. c
3. b 7. a
4. b 8. c

C. Reading Strategies
11. c 13. d 15. a
12. a 14. b

D. Elements of Literature
16. c 18. d 20. c
17. a 19. c

E. Vocabulary
21. b 23. b 25. a
22. a 24. b

F. Grammar/Usage
26. c 28. b 30. b
27. d 29. c

G. Writing Conventions
31. c 33. d 35. b
32. a 34. a

H. Editing
36. d 38. a 40. c
37. c 39. c

I. Writing
Answers will vary.

End-of-Book Exam

B. Reading Comprehension
1. d 5. b 9. a
2. a 6. d 10. a
3. d 7. d
4. b 8. c

C. Reading Strategies
11. b 13. a 15. c
12. c 14. b

D. Elements of Literature
16. a 18. b 20. a
17. d 19. c

E. Vocabulary
21. a 23. c 25. d
22. b 24. b

F. Grammar/Usage
26. a 28. b 30. c
27. c 29. a

G. Writing Conventions
31. a 33. a 35. d
32. d 34. b

H. Editing
36. b 38. d 40. a
37. a 39. b

I. Writing
Answers will vary.

Name ________________________________ Date ____________________________

Portfolio: Activity Rating and Reflection Sheet

Part I: Rating

Write the name of each activity in your work folder on the left. Think about how much you liked it. Circle one number for each activity.

Unit ___ Activities	I didn't like it.	I liked it a little.	I liked it.	I liked it very much.
______________________	1	2	3	4
______________________	1	2	3	4
______________________	1	2	3	4
______________________	1	2	3	4
______________________	1	2	3	4
______________________	1	2	3	4
______________________	1	2	3	4
______________________	1	2	3	4

Part II: Reflection

1. My Portfolio choice for Unit ___

I chose to put ______________________________ in my Portfolio because

____.

2. How I Learned

I learned best from . . .

___ listening and speaking. ___ reading. ___ writing.

I liked working . . .

___ by myself. ___ with a partner. ___ with a small group. ___ with the whole class.

Name ______________________________

Reading Fluency Chart

How many words did you read in one minute? Color in the graph up to the number of words that you read.
When you read silently, color in the chart with red. When you read orally, color in the chart with blue.

Words per Minute	Key: Silent Reading = Red Oral Reading = Blue																										
180																											
175																											
170																											
165																											
160																											
155																											
150																											
145																											
140																											
135																											
130																											
125																											
120																											
115																											
110																											
105																											
100																											
95																											
90																											
85																											
80																											
75																											
70																											
65																											
60																											
55																											
50																											
45																											
40																											
35																											
30																											
25																											
20																											
15																											
10																											
Reading Exercise	1	2	3	4	5	1	2	3	4	5	1	2	3	4	5	1	2	3	4	1	2	3	4	1	2	3	4
Unit	1					2					3					4				5				6			

Responding to Peers' Writing: *EQS*

***E*: Encourage**	***Q*: Question**	***S*: Suggestions**
• Help your partner recognize what he or she is doing right. • Be specific. Say things like: "I liked the surprise at the end the best." "You used some very interesting words in this sentence." "This poem made me think of my home."	• Ask questions when you would like more information. • Ask questions when something isn't clear. For example: "Why did your grandmother give you that picture?" "What do you mean, 'He went back'? Where did he go?"	• Ask your partner if he or she would like some suggestions. If your partner says "yes," offer suggestions to make the writing better. • Always let your partner choose whether or not to use your ideas. • Don't tell your partner what to do. Instead, make suggestions like: "You might try saying, 'My dog is fat' another way. How about 'My dog looks like a sausage with four legs'?" "What if you changed these two sentences around?"

Read your partner's selection. Use *EQS* to fill in the boxes.

Name ______________________ Partner's Name ______________________

***E*: Encourage**	***Q*: Question**	***S*: Suggestions**

Peer Editing Checklist

Use this checklist to edit your peer's writing.
You may also use it to check your own writing.

Writer's Name ______________________________

Editor's Name ______________________________

1. Is there a title? ______ Yes ______ No
2. Is the first sentence of each paragraph indented? ______ Yes ______ No
3. Does each sentence start with a capital letter? ______ Yes ______ No
4. Does each sentence end with a punctuation mark? ______ Yes ______ No
5. Does each name start with a capital letter? ______ Yes ______ No
6. Write one correct sentence from the paper.

   ____

7. Write one sentence that has a mistake.

   ____

8. Rewrite the sentence correctly.

   ____

Use these editing symbols:

¶	Start a new paragraph.
∧	Insert a word or words.
Sp	Correct a spelling error.
CAP	Use a capital letter.
lc	Use a lowercase letter.
p	Correct a punctuation error.
exact	Use a more exact word.
?	What does this mean?
∽	Transpose these letters.

Name ___________________________

Editor's Checklist

Use this checklist to proofread and revise your writing. Make a check in the box when you have edited your writing for each item. Give this checklist to your teacher with your writing assignment.

Edit for:	Student Check ☑	Teacher Comments	Score
I. Development of Ideas/Content **A.** Is the purpose of my writing clear? **B.** Is my writing focused on the topic I'm writing about? **C.** Did I support my ideas with details, facts, and examples? **D.** Did I write appropriately for my audience?	☐ ☐ ☐ ☐		
II. Organization **A.** Is my writing clear and logical? **B.** Do I have a strong, interesting beginning that gets the reader's attention? **C.** Are my ideas tied together? Do I use transitions? **D.** Do I have a strong ending that ties things together?	☐ ☐ ☐ ☐		
III. Sentence Structure **A.** Are my sentences complete? Do they have a subject and a verb? **B.** Did I make sure I don't have any run-on sentences or fragments? **C.** Did I use different types of sentences—compound and complex?	☐ ☐ ☐		
IV. Grammar and Usage **A.** Is my writing in the right tense (for example, present or past)? **B.** Did I use subject pronouns and object pronouns correctly—*I/me, he/him, she/her, we/us, they/them*? **C.** Did I use the pronouns *she, her,* or *hers* for women and girls and *he, him,* or *his* for men and boys? **D.** Do my verbs agree with their subjects? Did I use singular verbs with singular subjects and plural verbs with plural subjects?	☐ ☐ ☐ ☐		

Name ________________________________

Editor's Checklist (cont . . .)

Edit for:	Student Check ☑	Teacher Comments	Score
V. Word Choice **A.** Did I choose vivid and exact words? Did I use a thesaurus, glossary, or dictionary to help me choose better words? **B.** Did I eliminate extra words so that my writing is not wordy?	☐ ☐		
VI. Writing Conventions **Form** **A.** Did I write my name, the date, and a title on the page? **B.** Did I indent the first line of each paragraph? **C.** Did I include a bibliography and correctly cite any references that I used? **D.** Did I create an attractive computer presentation, or did I use my best handwriting? **Spelling** **E.** Did I check the spelling of all words I'm not sure about? **F.** If I wrote my paper on a computer, did I use spell check? **Capitalization** **G.** Did I capitalize the names of proper nouns, such as people's names and the names of cities and countries? **H.** Did I start each sentence with a capital letter? **Punctuation** **I.** Did I punctuate each sentence with the right mark (., ?, or !)? **J.** Did I put quotation marks around any direct speech? **K.** Did I use apostrophes correctly in contractions and possessives?	☐ ☐ ☐ ☐ ☐ ☐ ☐ ☐ ☐ ☐ ☐		
VII. My Own Criteria **A.** **B.** **C.**	☐ ☐ ☐		

Name ______________________________

Narrative Checklist

Use this checklist to evaluate your own writing and your classmates' writing.

__________ **Interesting title**

__________ **Name**

__________ **Date**

Introduction

1. __________ describes the setting
2. __________ introduces the characters
3. __________ introduces the problem or topic

Body

1. __________ describes an event
2. __________ gives details about the event
3. __________ uses sequence to relate events (throughout)

---

1. __________ describes an event
2. __________ gives details about the event
3. __________ uses strong verbs and vivid adjectives (throughout)

---

1. __________ brings problem to climax
2. __________ builds suspense for reader
3. __________ uses figurative language so the reader can "see," "taste," "hear," and "feel" the events (throughout)

Conclusion or Resolution

1. __________ restates problem
2. __________ shows how problem is resolved
3. __________ has a strong ending

________ I used the Editor's Checklist to edit and revise this narrative.

Name ____________________________________

Persuasive Checklist

Use this checklist to evaluate your own writing and your classmates' writing.

__________ **Interesting title**

__________ **Name**

__________ **Date**

Introduction

1. __________ asks a question
2. __________ answers a question
3. __________ gives 3 supporting reasons for answer

Body

1. __________ begins with "First, . . ."
2. __________ restates reason # 1
3. __________ gives three supporting details/examples

---

1. __________ begins with "Next, . . ."
2. __________ restates reason # 2
3. __________ gives three supporting details/examples

---

1. __________ begins with "Finally, . . ."
2. __________ restates reason # 3
3. __________ gives three supporting details/examples

Conclusion

1. __________ begins with "In conclusion . . ."
2. __________ restates introduction answer
3. __________ restates 3 supporting reasons

________ I used the Editor's Checklist to edit and revise this persuasive writing.

Name ______________________ Date ______________________

Oral Presentation Evaluation Sheet

Topic or Title ______________________

Presenter or Group ______________________

Did the presenter or group:	**lowest**		**mid**		**highest**
1. make use of eye contact and facial expressions?	1	2	3	4	5
2. have a good opening?	1	2	3	4	5
3. change the pitch and tone of voice?	1	2	3	4	5
4. use interesting and specific language?	1	2	3	4	5
5. use pauses or emphasis on key words?	1	2	3	4	5
6. support ideas with details and examples?	1	2	3	4	5
7. use gestures or action?	1	2	3	4	5
8. use visuals?	1	2	3	4	5
9. speak clearly?	1	2	3	4	5
10. have a good closing?	1	2	3	4	5
For a Reader's Theater or play					
11. wear costumes or use props?	1	2	3	4	5
12. act so I believed the story?	1	2	3	4	5

Name ______________________ Date ______________________

Speaker ______________________ Topic ______________________

Active Listening Checklist

Use this checklist to evaluate how well you listen and understand.

1. I liked ______________________ because ______________________

____

2. I want to know more about ______________________

____

3. I thought the opening was interesting. ____ Yes ____ No

4. The speaker stayed on the topic. ____ Yes ____ No

5. I did not understand ______________________

____

6. I needed the speaker to repeat or clarify ______________________

____

7. My own criteria: ______________________

____

8. My own criteria: ______________________

____

9. My own criteria: ______________________

____

Name ______________________________ Date ______________________

Topic ______________________________

Speaking Checklist

Use this checklist to evaluate your speaking.

1. Did I speak too slowly, too quickly, or just right? ______________________
2. Was the tone of my voice too high, too low, or just right? ______________
3. Did I speak loudly enough for the audience to hear me? ____ Yes ____ No
4. Did I produce the correct intonation patterns of sentences? ____ Yes ____ No
5. Did I have a good opening? ____ Yes ____ No
6. Did I look at my audience? ____ Yes ____ No
7. Did I speak with feeling? ____ Yes ____ No
8. Did I support my ideas with facts and examples? ____ Yes ____ No
9. Did I tell the audience how I feel about the topic? ____ Yes ____ No
10. Did I use interesting, specific words? ____ Yes ____ No
11. Did I use visuals to make the speech interesting? ____ Yes ____ No

My Own Criteria

12. ______________________________ ____ Yes ____ No
13. ______________________________ ____ Yes ____ No
14. ______________________________ ____ Yes ____ No

Name ______________________ Date ______________

Text/Presentation ______________________

Viewing Checklist

Visuals help you understand texts and presentations better. Analyzing visuals for their usefulness will help you to learn how to create good visuals. Think about these points as you view and create visuals.

1. Do I understand the purpose of this visual? ____ Yes ____ No
2. What is the purpose? ______________________

   ____
3. Does this visual help me to understand better? ____ Yes ____ No
4. How does it help me understand? ______________________

   ____
5. Is the visual labeled clearly? ____ Yes ____ No
6. Does the visual give me extra information? ____ Yes ____ No
7. What did I learn from the visual? ______________________

   ____
8. Would I create the same visual for this text/presentation? ____ Yes ____ No
9. What would I do differently? ______________________

   ____
10. My own viewing criteria: ______________________

    ____
11. My own viewing criteria: ______________________

    ____

Name ______________________ Date ______________

Word Study and Spelling

Keep a list of new words that you learn. Use a dictionary, a glossary, or the Newbury House Dictionary CD-ROM to find definitions.

Word	Page	Sentence from Reading	Definition	Your Sentence

Name ______________________ Date ______________

Word Study and Spelling Assessment Chart

1. Exchange your *Word Study and Spelling* pages with a partner.
2. Choose five words and ask your partner to spell them on a piece of paper.
3. Choose another five words and ask your partner to write a sentence using each.
4. Check your partner's work.
5. Record the number of words spelled correctly in the first row of your partner's chart.
6. Record the number of words used correctly in a sentence in the second row.
7. Record the words that were spelled or used incorrectly in the third row.

My Score	Unit 1	Unit 2	Unit 3	Unit 4	Unit 5	Unit 6
How many words did I spell correctly?	Correct: Incorrect:	Correct: Incorrect:	Correct: Incorrect:	Correct: Incorrect:	Correct: Incorrect:	Correct: Incorrect:
How many words did I use in a sentence correctly?	Correct: Incorrect:	Correct: Incorrect:	Correct: Incorrect:	Correct: Incorrect:	Correct: Incorrect:	Correct: Incorrect:
Which words do I need to study?						

Name ______________________ Date ______________________

Activity and Project Reflection

Think about the activities and projects that you have done in class. Then answer these questions.

1. The most interesting activity or project that we did was ______________________
____

2. I think this activity or project was interesting because ______________________
____
____
____
____

3. In this activity or project, I learned ______________________
____
____
____
____

4. Did anyone else work with you or help you with your learning? How did he or she help you? ______________________
____
____
____
____

Test-Taking Tips

Use these tips to help you improve your performance on tests.

BEFORE THE TEST

1. Complete all of your assignments on time.
2. Take notes in class as you go over your assignments.
3. Save and review your class notes, assignments, and quizzes.
4. Ask your teacher what topics will be covered on the test.
5. Ask your teacher what kind of test you will take. For example, will the questions be true/false, multiple choice, or essay?
6. Be organized. Make a study guide. Making note cards or rewriting information will help you review.
7. Study, and then get a good night's sleep before the test.
8. Eat a good, healthy breakfast on the day of the test.
9. Bring everything that you need to the test (pencils, erasers, pens, and so on).

DURING THE TEST

1. Pay close attention to the teacher's instructions. Ask questions if you do not understand.
2. Read the instructions on the test carefully.
3. Look at the test before you begin to see how long it is.
4. Don't spend too much time on any one section or question. Skip questions that you don't know. Return to them if you have time at the end.
5. Watch the time to make sure you finish the whole test.
6. Save time to look over the test before you turn it in. Don't worry if other students finish before you. Use all the time that you have.

AFTER THE TEST

1. When your test is returned to you, look at it carefully.
2. Look up the answers to any questions you left blank or got wrong.
3. Ask your teacher about any questions that you still don't understand. The same question might appear again on another test.

Test-Taking Tips (cont . . .)

TYPES OF TEST QUESTIONS

TRUE/FALSE STATEMENTS

Decide if the following statement is *true* or *false.*

False 1. All trees lose their leaves in the winter.

1. Read the statements carefully.
2. Look for anything in the statement that is not true. If any detail is false, then the whole statement is false.
3. Watch out for absolute words like *always, all, never, no, best,* and *worst.* These may be clues that the statement is false.

MULTIPLE-CHOICE QUESTIONS

Choose the correct answer from the list of choices.

1. Which type of tree loses its leaves in the fall? **a.** coniferous tree **b.** pine tree (**c.**) deciduous tree **d.** fir tree

1. Read the question carefully before you look at the answer choices.
2. Answer the question before you look at the choices. Then see if your answer is listed.
3. Read all of the answers before you choose one.
4. If you are not sure which answer is correct, cross out the ones that you know are wrong. Choose one of the answers that is left.

ESSAY QUESTIONS

Write one or more paragraphs to answer the question.s

1. Describe three things that happen to deciduous trees in the fall.

1. Know what you are being asked to do (for example, *describe, discuss, compare, explain,* and so on).
2. Plan your essay before you begin to write. Making a basic outline first will help you stay focused.
3. Include a *thesis statement, supporting evidence,* and a *conclusion.*
4. Show how much you know, but stay focused. Include only information that is relevant to your topic or thesis.
5. Write neatly. Your teacher must be able to read your answer.

Lesson Plan Checklist

for *The Sheltered Instruction Observation Protocol*

I. PREPARATION

_______ Write content objectives clearly for students.

_______ Write language objectives clearly for students.

_______ Choose content concepts appropriate for age and educational background level of students.

_______ Identify supplementary materials to use (graphs, models, visuals).

_______ Adapt content (e.g., text, assignment) to all levels of student proficiency.

_______ Plan meaningful activities that integrate lesson concepts (e.g., surveys, letter writing, simulations, constructing models) with language practice opportunities for reading, writing, listening, and/or speaking.

II. INSTRUCTION

Building Background

_______ Explicitly link concepts to students' backgrounds and experiences.

_______ Explicitly link past learning and new concepts.

_______ Emphasize key vocabulary (e.g., introduce, write, repeat, and highlight for students to see).

Comprehensible Input

_______ Use speech appropriate for students' proficiency level (e.g., slower rate, enunciation, and simple sentence structure for beginners).

_______ Explain academic tasks clearly.

_______ Use a variety of techniques to make content concepts clear (e.g., modeling, visuals, hands-on activities, demonstrations, gestures, body language).

Strategies

_______ Provide ample opportunities for students to use strategies (e.g., problem solving, predicting, organizing, summarizing, categorizing, evaluating, self-monitoring).

_______ Use scaffolding techniques consistently (providing the right amount of support to move students from one level of understanding to a higher level) throughout the lesson.

_______ Use a variety of question types throughout the lesson, including those that promote higher-order thinking skills throughout the lesson (e.g., literal, analytical, and interpretive questions).

Short, D., and Ecchevaria, J. (1999). *The Sheltered Instruction Observation Protocol: A Tool for Teacher-Researcher Collaboration and Professional Development.* Center for Research on Education, Diversity & Excellence, University of California, Santa Cruz.

Lesson Plan Checklist (cont . . .)

for *The Sheltered Instruction Observation Protocol*

Interaction

________ Provide frequent opportunities for interaction and discussion between teacher/student and among students about lessons and concepts, and encourage elaborated responses.

________ Use group configurations that support language and content objectives of the lesson.

________ Consistently provide sufficient wait time for student responses.

________ Give ample opportunities for students to clarify key concepts in L1 as needed with aide, peer, or L1 text.

Practice/Application

________ Provide hands-on materials and/or manipulatives for students to practice using new content knowledge.

________ Provide activities for students to apply content and language knowledge in the classroom.

________ Use activities that integrate all language skills (reading, writing, listening, and speaking).

Lesson Delivery

________ Support content objectives clearly.

________ Support language objectives clearly.

________ Engage students approximately 90–100% of the period (with most students taking part in and working on task throughout the lesson).

________ Pace the lesson appropriately to the students' ability level.

Review/Assessment

________ Give a comprehensive review of key vocabulary.

________ Give a comprehensive review of key content concepts.

________ Provide feedback to students regularly on their output (e.g., language, content, work).

________ Conduct assessments of student comprehension and learning throughout lesson on all lesson objectives (e.g., spot checking, group response) throughout the lesson.

Short, D., and Ecchevaria, J. (1999). *The Sheltered Instruction Observation Protocol: A Tool for Teacher-Researcher Collaboration and Professional Development.* Center for Research on Education, Diversity & Excellence, University of California, Santa Cruz.

Rubric for Oral Reading Fluency

adapted from the National Assessment of Educational Progress (NAEP)
Scale for Assessing Oral Reading Fluency

Point Scale	Description of Oral Reading Fluency
4	Reads primarily in large, meaningful phrase groups. Although some regressions, repetitions, and deviations from text may be present, these do not appear to detract from the overall structure of the story. Preservation of the author's syntax is consistent. Some or most of the story is read with expressive interpretation.
3	Reads primarily in three- or four-word phrase groups. Some smaller groupings may be present. However, the majority of phrasing seems appropriate and preserves the syntax of the author. Little or no expressive interpretation is present.
2	Reads primarily in two-word phrases with some three- or four-word groupings. Some word-by-word reading may be present. Word groupings may seem awkward and unrelated to the larger context of the sentence or passage.
1	Reads primarily word by word. Occasional two-word or three-word phrases may occur, but these are infrequent and/or they do not preserve meaningful syntax.